MESON THEORY OF NUCLEAR FORCES

WOLFGANG PAULI
THE INSTITUTE FOR ADVANCED STUDY, PRINCETON, NEW JERSEY, AND FEDERAL POLYTECHNICUM ZURICH, SWITZERLAND

1946
INTERSCIENCE PUBLISHERS, INC.
NEW YORK

INTERSCIENCE PUBLISHERS, INC.
215 Fourth Avenue, New York 3, N.Y.

Printed in the United States of America
by Mack Printing Company, Easton, Pa.

PREFACE

The purpose of this volume is to make accessible to a larger number of readers the lectures which I gave in the autumn of 1944 at the Massachusetts Institute of Technology. Without pretending to contain anything essentially new, they may serve to give to students and research workers a first orientation in the more recent literature on the theory of the interaction of mesons with protons and neutrons (nucleons) and the interactions between nucleons derived from it. Despite the imperfections of my lectures, the original notes written by Dr. J. F. Carlson and Dr. A. J. F. Siegert have been amended only slightly, to preserve the informal character of the lectures and to emphasize the very provisional state of the problems in question, to which new experiments may in the future make important contributions. Special thanks are extended to Dr. S. T. Ma for reading and checking the proofs.

Princeton, New Jersey — WOLFGANG PAULI
February, 1946

CONTENTS

CHAPTER I

The meson theory of nuclear forces has been developed in analogy to the theory of the Coulomb force, which arises from the interaction of charged particles with the electromagnetic field. The short range of the nuclear forces is obtained by letting the particles corresponding to the photons have a rest mass,[1] the range of forces arising from a field of particles of rest mass μ being $\hbar/\mu c$. From experiments on scattering of neutrons by protons the range of nuclear forces is known to be $\sim 2 \times 10^{-13}$ cm, which leads to a rest mass $\mu \sim 200$ electron masses. Charged particles of this rest mass have subsequently been discovered in cosmic rays.

Another difference between the meson field and the electromagnetic field lies in the fact that mesons have charge and spin.

The main experimental data to be explained by the meson theory of nuclear forces are:

(*a*) the binding energy of the deuteron: $E_0 = 2.17$ Mev,

(*b*) the cross section for neutron–proton[2] scattering: $\sigma = (21 \pm 0.7) \times 10^{-24}$ cm^2,

(*c*) the quadrupole moment of the deuteron: $Q = 2.73 \times 10^{-27}$ cm^2

[1] H. Yukawa, *Proc. Phys.-Math. Soc. Japan*, **17,** 48 (1935).

[2] H. Hanstein, *Phys. Rev.*, **57,** 1045 (1940).

(*d*) the analysis of the proton–proton scattering shows that in the singlet state the interaction energy of two protons is, in very good approximation, the same as that between a proton and a neutron.

The nuclear forces must be dependent on the spins of the heavy particles, since the singlet state formed in the scattering of neutrons by protons is a virtual state and thus is higher than the triplet ground state of the deuteron by more than the binding energy of the deuteron.

The force needed—in addition to the Coulomb force—to explain the proton–proton scattering is practically the same as the force between proton and neutron. It would, therefore, be possible to explain nuclear forces with neutral mesons only. Since, however, the mesons found in cosmic rays are charged mesons, it seems more satisfactory to include charged mesons in the theory of nuclear forces. The assumption of charged mesons only, without neutral mesons, leads to difficulties in that, in first approximation, it does not give rise to forces between like particles.

Another difference between electromagnetic and meson-field theory is found in the fact that for charged particles at rest the term in the force quadratic in their charge gives the force exactly, namely the Coulomb force. For charged mesons the term quadratic in the coupling constant is only an approximation, even if the heavy particles are at rest. This corresponds to the fact that photons are not scattered by particles held at rest, while mesons are scattered by fixed heavy particles, since spin and charge do not stay "at rest."

The difficulty of electromagnetic mass appears in the meson theory even for fixed particles as the difficulty of inertia of spin and charge.

Various Types of Meson Fields

The heavy particles are characterized by wave functions ψ_N and ψ_P where the indices N, P indicate the two charge states, neutron and proton, of the nucleon (heavy particle). The operators of charge creation τ_+ and charge annihilation τ_- act on ψ as follows:

$$\tau_+\psi_N = \psi_P \qquad \tau_-\psi_P = \psi_N$$
$$\tau_+\psi_P = 0 \qquad \tau_-\psi_N = 0$$

where ψ_P and ψ_N are understood to mean

$$\psi_P = \binom{\psi}{0} \quad \text{and} \quad \psi_N = \binom{0}{\psi}$$

In this system the operators τ_+ and τ_- are, therefore, represented by the matrices

$$\tau_+ = \begin{pmatrix} 0 & 1 \\ 0 & 0 \end{pmatrix} \qquad \tau_- = \begin{pmatrix} 0 & 0 \\ 1 & 0 \end{pmatrix}$$

with the properties

$$\tau_+^2 = \tau_-^2 = 0$$
$$\tau_-\tau_+ + \tau_+\tau_- = 1$$

We further introduce the operators

$$\tau_1 = \tau_+ + \tau_-$$
$$\tau_2 = -i(\tau_+ - \tau_-)$$
$$\tau_3 = \tau_+\tau_- - \tau_-\tau_+$$

τ_1, τ_2, τ_3 have the same properties as the spin operators for spin $\frac{1}{2}$ and are called the "isotopic spin."

The meson field is represented by the operators of

creation φ^* and annihilation φ of a meson, so that the operator $\tau_-\varphi^*$, for instance, changes a proton into a neutron and creates a meson of positive charge. Instead of φ and φ^* we shall sometimes use φ_1 and φ_2, defined by

$$\varphi = (\varphi_1 - i\varphi_2)/\sqrt{2} \qquad \varphi^* = (\varphi_1 + i\varphi_2)/\sqrt{2}$$

Scalar Charged Meson Field

The field energy of the meson field alone is written[3] as

$$H_0 = \tfrac{1}{2}\sum_\alpha \int [\pi_\alpha{}^2 + (\nabla\varphi_\alpha)^2 + \mu^2\varphi_\alpha{}^2]dV$$

and the interaction energy

$$H_{\text{int}} = \sqrt{4\pi}\, g \sum_{A,\alpha} \tau_\alpha^A \varphi_\alpha(Z^A)$$

where A (and in subsequent equations, B) denotes the heavy particles and Z^A the position of the heavy particles. From the Hamiltonian $H = H_0 + H_{\text{int}}$, the equations of motion are derived as follows:

$$\delta H/\delta\varphi_\alpha = -\dot{\Pi}_\alpha = -\nabla^2\varphi_\alpha + \mu^2\varphi_\alpha + \sqrt{4\pi}\, g \sum_A \tau_\alpha^A \delta(X - Z^A)$$

$$\delta H/\delta\Pi_\alpha = \dot{\varphi}_\alpha = \Pi_\alpha$$

where δ indicates variational differentiation. Combining the equations of motion yields the Kirchhoff equation of the scalar meson field

$$-\nabla^2\varphi_\alpha + \mu^2\varphi_\alpha + \frac{\partial^2\varphi_\alpha}{\partial t^2} = -\sqrt{4\pi}\, g \sum_A \tau_\alpha^A \delta(X - Z^A)$$

Neglecting the time variation of the operators τ_α^A, one obtains a static solution for φ_α:

[3] All equations are written with natural units, i.e., $\hbar$ and $c = 1$.

$$(\varphi_\alpha)_{\text{stat}} = -\frac{g}{\sqrt{4\pi}} \sum_A \tau_\alpha^A \frac{e^{-\mu r}}{r}$$

where $r = |\mathbf{X} - \mathbf{Z}^A|$.

Substituting this solution into H_{int} we have

$$(H_{\text{int}})_{\text{stat}} = -g^2 \sum_{AB} \sum_\alpha \tau_\alpha^A \tau_\alpha^B e^{-\mu r_{AB}}/r_{AB}$$

with $r_{AB} = |\mathbf{Z}^A - \mathbf{Z}^B|$, so that the potential energy between two nucleons is

$$V_{AB} = -g^2 \sum_\alpha (\tau_\alpha^A \tau_\alpha^B)\, e^{-\mu r_{AB}}/r_{AB}$$

If only charged mesons are assumed, α has the values 1 and 2, and we have

$$\sum_{\alpha=1,2} \tau_\alpha^A \tau_\alpha^B = 2(\tau_+^A \tau_-^B + \tau_-^A \tau_+^B)$$

with τ_1 and τ_2 as previously defined.

It is therefore

$$\sum_{\alpha=1,2} \tau_\alpha^A \tau_\alpha^B = \begin{cases} 0 \text{ for equal nucleons} \\ 2 \times \text{exchange of charge operator for} \\ \text{unequal nucleons} \end{cases}$$

[for instance:

$$2(\tau_+^A \tau_-^B + \tau_-^A \tau_+^B)\psi_P^A \psi_P^B = 0 \text{ because } \tau_+ \psi_P = 0$$
$$2(\tau_+^A \tau_-^B + \tau_-^A \tau_+^B)\psi_P^A \psi_N^B = 2\psi_N^A \psi_P^B]$$

This form of the theory, therefore, does not explain forces between like particles, but holds only in terms of a g^2 approximation. There are forces of order g^4 and of higher orders between like particles and, in strong coupling theories, these forces may be as strong as the g^2 forces.

Pseudoscalar Symmetric Theory

As mentioned above, the spin dependence of nuclear forces is necessary to explain the energy difference between the triplet and singlet state of the deuteron. The spin dependence can be achieved by introducing a pseudoscalar meson field, and forces between like nucleons are obtained by introducing neutral mesons. The unperturbed Hamiltonian of the meson field is

$$H_0 = \tfrac{1}{2} \sum_{\alpha} \int dV \{ \Pi_\alpha^2 + (\nabla \varphi_\alpha)^2 + \mu_0^2 \varphi_\alpha^2 \}$$

and the interaction part is assumed to be

$$H_{\text{int}} = -\sqrt{4\pi} \sum_{A\alpha} \tau_\alpha f_0 \cdot (\boldsymbol{\sigma}_A \cdot \nabla) \varphi_\alpha (Z_A)$$

where f_0 is the coupling constant with the dimension of a length, and the $\boldsymbol{\sigma}_A$ are the spin operators operating on the wave functions describing the nucleons. α runs from 1 to 3 for charged and neutral mesons. This form of H_{int} has been chosen because it is the simplest way of introducing spin dependent forces. The equations of motion are obtained in the same way as before and, combined, yield

$$\left(-\nabla^2 + \mu_0^2 + \frac{\partial^2}{\partial t^2} \right) \varphi_\alpha = -\tau_\alpha \sum_{A} \sqrt{4\pi} f_0 \cdot (\boldsymbol{\sigma}_A \cdot \nabla) \delta(X - Z_A)$$

The potential energy for the interaction of two nucleons is obtained in the same way as before:

$$V_{AB} = f_0^2 T_{AB} (\boldsymbol{\sigma}_A \cdot \nabla)(\boldsymbol{\sigma}_B \cdot \nabla)\, e^{-\mu_0 r_{AB}}/r_{AB}$$

where

$$T_{AB} = \sum_{\alpha=1,2,3} \tau_\alpha^A \tau_\alpha^B = \begin{cases} -3 \text{ for charge-antisymmetric states} \\ +1 \text{ for charge-symmetric states} \end{cases}$$

An example of a charge-antisymmetric state is the ground state of the deuteron, which is symmetric in orbit and spin and, therefore, antisymmetric in the charge, while the singlet state of the deuteron is spin-antisymmetric and orbit-symmetric, and, therefore, charge-symmetric.

Carrying out the differentiations we have

$$(\boldsymbol{\sigma}_A \cdot \boldsymbol{\nabla})(\boldsymbol{\sigma}_B \cdot \boldsymbol{\nabla}) \frac{e^{-\mu r_{AB}}}{r_{AB}} = \frac{1}{3} S_{AB} \left(\frac{3}{r^3} + \frac{3\mu}{r^2} + \frac{\mu^2}{r} \right) e^{-\mu r} + \frac{1}{3} \sum\nolimits_{AB} \cdot \frac{\mu^2}{r} e^{-\mu r}$$

where

$$S_{AB} = 3(\boldsymbol{\sigma}_A \cdot \mathbf{n})(\boldsymbol{\sigma}_B \cdot \mathbf{n}) - (\boldsymbol{\sigma}_A \cdot \boldsymbol{\sigma}_B), \quad \mathbf{n} = (\mathbf{X}_A - \mathbf{X}_B)/r_{AB}$$

and

$$\sum\nolimits_{AB} = (\boldsymbol{\sigma}_A \cdot \boldsymbol{\sigma}_B)$$

The existence of the tensor force S_{AB} explains the existence and sign of the quadrupole moment. The high singularity of V_{AB} at $r_{AB} = 0$, however, makes the solution of the Schrödinger equation impossible. Bethe[4] has suggested cutting off at a small value of r_{AB}; in this way, one can actually explain the experimental data *a*, *b*, and *c*. It should, however, be noted that one then has three constants available, namely, μ_0, f_0, and the cutting-off radius.

Scattering of high-energy neutrons on protons is not in agreement with the pseudoscalar symmetrical theory. Hulthén[5] shows that a mixture between scalar neutral meson field and pseudoscalar charged meson field

[4] H. A. Bethe, *Phys. Rev.*, **57**, 260, 390 (1940).

[5] L. Hulthén, *Kgl. Fysiograf. Sällskap. Lund Förh.*, **14**, No. 2 (1944).

avoids this discrepancy. His theory has the further consequence that there is no tensor force between like nucleons, because the pseudoscalar charged mesons do not contribute to the interaction of like nucleons in the g^2 approximation. This is no objection to his theory since there is no experimental evidence for such a tensor force in the low-energy scattering experiments, which are the only ones available to the present time. Even if there were a tensor force between like nucleons, it could not be effective in these low-energy experiments since low energy implies orbital symmetry, and the likeness of the particles implies charge symmetry, so that the scattering must be described by a wave function antisymmetric in the spins. The tensor force S_{AB} vanishes when it is applied to a spin-antisymmetric wave function. Experiments on high-energy scattering of like particles would therefore be required to test Hulthén's theory.[6]

Instead of cutting off, Møller and Rosenfeld used a mixture of vector and pseudoscalar fields, a scheme which was improved by Schwinger.

Vector-Field Theory[7]

The Hamiltonian for the unperturbed field is

$$H_0 = \frac{1}{2} \sum_{\alpha} \int dV \left\{ \Pi_\alpha{}^2 + \frac{1}{\mu^2} (\nabla \cdot \Pi_\alpha)^2 + (\mathrm{curl}\, \psi_\alpha)^2 + \mu_1{}^2 \psi_\alpha{}^2 \right\}$$

The interaction part of the Hamiltonian is assumed to be

[6] The saturation question in connection with this hypothesis is discussed by L. Hulthén, *Phys. Rev.*, **67,** 193 (1945).

[7] N. Kemmer, *Proc. Roy. Soc. London*, **A166,** 127 (1938). H. J. Bhabha, *ibid.*, **A166,** 501 (1938).

$$H_{\text{int}} = -\sqrt{4\pi} \sum_{A\alpha} \tau_\alpha [f_1 \cdot (\boldsymbol{\sigma}_A \cdot \text{curl}) \boldsymbol{\psi}(Z_A) + g_1 \text{ div } \boldsymbol{\psi}(Z_A)]$$

where f_1 and g_1 are the coupling constants. The interaction energy between two nucleons is then found to be

$$V_{AB} = T_{AB}\{-(\boldsymbol{\sigma}_A \cdot \nabla)(\boldsymbol{\sigma}_B \cdot \nabla) f_1^2 (e^{-\mu_1 r_{AB}}/r_{AB}) + (\Sigma_{AB} f_1^2 + g_1^2)\mu_1^2 \, e^{-\mu_1 r_{AB}}/r_{AB}\}$$

The tensor force is the same as in the pseudoscalar theory, except for the opposite sign. This makes the sign of the quadrupole moment wrong; the vector-field theory alone is therefore ruled out.

Møller and Rosenfeld mix the pseudoscalar and vector fields, assuming $f_1 = f_0$ and $\mu_1 = \mu_0$. In their theory, therefore, the tensor forces are completely cancelled, and the quadrupole moment vanishes.

Schwinger retains $f_1 = f_0$, but takes $\mu_1 > \mu_0$, so as to eliminate only the singularities higher than r_{AB}^{-1} and to obtain the correct sign of the quadrupole moment. The interaction energy is then

$$V_{AB} = \frac{1}{3} T_{AB} \left\{ S_{AB} f_0^2 \left[\left(\frac{3}{r^3} + \frac{3\mu_0}{r^2} + \frac{\mu_0^2}{r} \right) e^{-\mu_0 r} - \left(\frac{3}{r^3} + \frac{3\mu_1}{r^2} + \frac{\mu_1^2}{r} \right) e^{-\mu_1 r} \right] + \Sigma_{AB} f_0^2 \left[\mu_0^2 \frac{e^{-\mu_0 r}}{r} + 2\mu_1^2 \frac{e^{-\mu_1 r}}{r} \right] + 3 g_1^2 \mu_1^2 \frac{e^{-\mu_1 r}}{r} \right\}$$

Jauch and Hu[8] have solved the Schrödinger equation for this potential energy and find that under the assumption $g_1 = 0$ the binding energy of the deuteron and proton–neutron scattering cross section are obtained correctly by using $\mu_1/\mu_0 = 1.6$ and $f_0\mu_0 = 0.226$

[8] J. M. Jauch and N. Hu, *Phys. Rev.*, 65, 289 (1944).

With this choice of constants they obtain for the quadrupole moment of the deuteron, however, the value 0.926×10^{-27} cm^2, instead of the experimental value of 2.73×10^{-27} cm^2. If one assumes g_1 to be different from zero this discrepancy becomes even worse.

Hulthén[9] has attempted to compute the quadrupole moment of the deuteron for the M–R mixture by taking into account the first order relativistic effect in the interaction energy between mesons and nucleons. The relativistic corrections thus obtained are large but cannot be trusted because the approximation used is equivalent to an expansion in terms of $(1/M)\nabla$, where M is the nucleon mass, and therefore introduces higher and higher singularities in the interaction potential between two nucleons.

The use of the rigorous relativistic form of the interaction between nucleons and the meson field and the taking into account of the recoil energy of the nucleons in the intermediate states does not improve the situation because even in all "mixed" theories singularities of the type r_{AB}^{-2} and r_{AB}^{-3} reappear.[10] The necessity of "cutting off" remains then even in the mixed theory, so that nothing is gained by the mixing.

[9] L. Hulthén, *Arkiv. Mat. Astron. Fysik*, **A29**, No. 33 (1943).
[10] N. Hu, *Phys. Rev.*, **67**, 339 (1945).

CHAPTER II

The nuclear forces considered in the first lecture were based on perturbation calculations, taking into account only terms quadratic in the coupling constant. But the discussion of higher-order terms leads to more than just mathematical difficulties. For point-source nucleons the theory is not convergent, as each step in the successive approximations results in higher and higher singularities and infinities. On the other hand the assumption of a finite source which makes the theory convergent is in contradiction with the relativistic invariance of the theory, unless particular tricks of subtraction are applied.

The concept of a finite source can be brought into field theories in two different ways. In electromagnetic theory, for instance, a radius "a" of the charged particle can be introduced as a minimum radius inside of which the Coulomb field does not hold. The electromagnetic mass can be calculated from this radius a. As an alternative, one could assume the Coulomb field to stay formally valid everywhere, but replace infinite terms in the interaction energy by newly chosen mechanical constants.

In meson theory a mechanical constant $1/a$ of dimension length^{-1} can be chosen; it is found to determine the "spin inertia," that is, the reaction of the eigenfield of the nucleon to the motion of its spin. Unlike the electron mass, the spin inertia is not experimentally known. But we shall see that it cannot be zero, because this assumption would lead to wrong values for the magnetic moments of the nucleons. The assumption of large spin inertia leads to the so-called "strong coupling" case and results in the existence of excited states (isobars) of the nucleon with higher values of the spin. Effects involving the spin, similar to those mentioned here, result from the interaction of charged meson fields with the "isotopic spin" of the nucleons. The same constant a^{-1} will, in fact, determine also a "charge inertia" and in these theories excited states of the nucleon with higher values of the charge will exist.

Experimentally, the existence of such isobars should affect experiments on high-energy 30–40 Mev scattering of nucleons on nucleons. If these stable isobars exist they should be created in scattering processes, where the incident neutrons have an energy larger than, or equal to, twice the excitation energy of the isobars.

Theory of Extended Source

In this theory the heavy particle is assumed to be at rest. For the meson field, which of course must be treated relativistically, the neutral pseudoscalar case is chosen for simplicity. The Hamiltonian for the meson field in interaction with one nucleon is

$$H = \tfrac{1}{2}\Big[\int \{\pi^2 + (\nabla\varphi)^2 + \mu^2\varphi^2\} d^3x + \sqrt{4\pi}\, f \int U(\mathbf{x})(\boldsymbol{\sigma}\cdot\nabla)\varphi d^3x\Big]$$

where d^3x denotes the volume element in x-space, and the integration extends over all space. For $U(\mathbf{x})$ we only assume now $\int U(\mathbf{x})d^3x = 1$. For a point source, $U(\mathbf{x})$ would be a δ-function.

We shall now perfoım a transformation to momentum space by means of the following equations:

$$U(\mathbf{x}) = (2\pi)^{-3}\int v(\mathbf{k})e^{i\mathbf{k}\cdot\mathbf{x}}d^3k$$

with

$$v(\mathbf{k}) = \int U(\mathbf{x})e^{-i\mathbf{k}\cdot\mathbf{x}}d^3x$$

From the normalization of $U(\mathbf{x})$ follows $v(0) = 1$. The wave functions are transformed as follows:

$$\varphi(\mathbf{x}) = (2\pi)^{-3/2}\int q(\mathbf{k})e^{i\mathbf{k}\cdot\mathbf{x}}d^3k$$

with

$$q(\mathbf{k}) = (2\pi)^{-3/2}\int \varphi(\mathbf{x})e^{-i\mathbf{k}\cdot\mathbf{x}}d^3x$$

and

$$\pi(\mathbf{x}) = (2\pi)^{-3/2}\int p(\mathbf{k})e^{-i\mathbf{k}\cdot\mathbf{x}}d^3k$$

with

$$p(\mathbf{k}) = (2\pi)^{-3/2}\int \pi(\mathbf{x})e^{i\mathbf{k}\cdot\mathbf{x}}d^3x$$

We further define

$$\begin{aligned} \tilde{q}(\mathbf{k}) &= q(\mathbf{k})v(-\mathbf{k}) \\ \tilde{p}(\mathbf{k}) &= p(\mathbf{k})/v(-\mathbf{k}) \\ G(\mathbf{k}) &= v(\mathbf{k})\,v(-\mathbf{k}) \end{aligned}$$

In its original meaning, U, describing the extension of a nucleon in space, should be real. Then $v(-\mathbf{k})$ must be equal to $v^*(\mathbf{k})$, and $G(\mathbf{k})$ is positive. We shall, in the following, generalize by assuming G real but not necessarily positive. This generalization is possible in momentum space, and as long as one does not consider quantities like the spatial densities of mesons. While with this generalization U is not necessarily real, H

can still be kept real, as long as $\tilde{q}(-\mathbf{k}) = \tilde{q}^*(\mathbf{k})$. We find for H:

$$H = \frac{1}{2}\Big[\int d^3x(2\pi)^{-3}\Big\{\int\int p(\mathbf{k})\, p(\mathbf{k}')\, e^{-i(\mathbf{k}+\mathbf{k}')\cdot\mathbf{x}}d^3kd^3k' +$$

$$\int\int[-(\mathbf{k}\cdot\mathbf{k}') + \mu^2]\; q(\mathbf{k})q(\mathbf{k}')e^{i(\mathbf{k}+\mathbf{k}')\cdot\mathbf{x}}d^3kd^3k'\Big\} + \sqrt{4\pi}\, f\times$$

$$\int d^3x(2\pi)^{-3}\int v(\mathbf{k}')e^{i\mathbf{k}'\mathbf{x}}d^3k'\int(\boldsymbol{\sigma}\cdot i\mathbf{k}')(2\pi)^{-3/2}q(\mathbf{k})e^{i\mathbf{k}\cdot\mathbf{x}}d^3k\Big]$$

$$= \frac{1}{2}\Big[\int p(\mathbf{k})p(-\mathbf{k})d^3k + \int(\mu^2 + k^2)q(\mathbf{k})q(-\mathbf{k})d^3k +$$

$$\frac{if}{\sqrt{2}\cdot\pi}\int(\boldsymbol{\sigma}\cdot\mathbf{k})\; q(\mathbf{k})\; v(-\mathbf{k})d^3k\Big]$$

$$= \frac{1}{2}\Big[\int\Big\{G(\mathbf{k})\tilde{p}(\mathbf{k})\tilde{p}(-\mathbf{k}) + \frac{k_0{}^2}{G(\mathbf{k})}\,\tilde{q}(\mathbf{k})\tilde{q}(-\mathbf{k})\Big\}\, d^3k +$$

$$\frac{if}{\pi\sqrt{2}}\int(\boldsymbol{\sigma}\cdot\mathbf{k})\tilde{q}(\mathbf{k})\; d^3k\Big]$$

with $k_0{}^2 = k^2 + \mu^2$.

This Hamiltonian yields the following equations of motion:

$$-\frac{\delta H}{\delta\tilde{q}} = \dot{\tilde{p}}(\mathbf{k}) = -\frac{k_0{}^2}{G(\mathbf{k})}\,\tilde{q}(-\mathbf{k}) - \frac{if}{\sqrt{2}\pi}\;(\boldsymbol{\sigma}\cdot\mathbf{k})$$

or

$$\dot{\tilde{p}}(-\mathbf{k}) = -\frac{k_0{}^2}{G(\mathbf{k})}\,\tilde{q}(\mathbf{k}) + \frac{if}{\sqrt{2}\pi}\,(\boldsymbol{\sigma}\cdot\mathbf{k})$$

and

$$\dot{\tilde{q}}(\mathbf{k}) = \frac{\delta H}{\delta\tilde{p}(\mathbf{k})} = G(\mathbf{k})\tilde{p}(-\mathbf{k})$$

Combining these two equations yields

$$\frac{\partial^2 q\,(\mathbf{k})}{\partial t^2} + k_0{}^2\tilde{q}\,(\mathbf{k}) = \frac{if}{\pi\sqrt{2}}\,G(\mathbf{k})(\boldsymbol{\sigma}\cdot\mathbf{k}) \qquad (1)$$

this being the Kirchhoff equation in momentum space.

From the Hamiltonian one can also derive the equation of motion of the spin. We shall, in the following, treat the spin as a classical unit vector, with the property

$$[\sigma_x, \sigma_y] = -2\sigma_z \quad \text{(and cyclic permutation)}$$

where [ ] denotes the classical Poisson bracket. We obtain as the equation of motion

$$\dot{\boldsymbol{\sigma}} = [H, \boldsymbol{\sigma}]$$

For instance

$$\dot{\boldsymbol{\sigma}}_x = \frac{if}{\pi\sqrt{2}} \int \tilde{q}\,(\mathbf{k})\, d^3k\, [(\boldsymbol{\sigma}\cdot\mathbf{k}), \sigma_x]$$

and with

$$\begin{aligned} [(\boldsymbol{\sigma}\cdot\mathbf{k}), \sigma_x] &= [\sigma_x k_x + \sigma_y k_y + \sigma_z k_z, \sigma_x] \\ &= +\,2\sigma_z k_y - 2\sigma_y k_z = 2[\mathbf{k} \times \boldsymbol{\sigma}]_x \end{aligned}$$

we have

$$\dot{\boldsymbol{\sigma}} = -\frac{\sqrt{2}\, if}{\pi}\left[\boldsymbol{\sigma} \times \int \mathbf{k}\tilde{q}\,(\mathbf{k}) d^3k\right] \qquad (2)$$

We shall now attempt to solve Equations (1) and (2) and to apply the solutions to two cases:

(1) Free gyration of the nucleon. This gyration corresponds, when quantized, to isobars of total spin $\frac{1}{2}$, $\frac{3}{2}$, etc., where the total angular momentum of field and nucleon, not that of the nucleon alone, is conserved.

(2) Scattering of mesons by nucleons. The scattering is described as follows: The incident meson wave

moves the spin, the moving spin radiates outgoing meson waves.

For abbreviation we define a vector

$$\mathbf{F} = -\frac{i\sqrt{2}}{\pi} f \int \mathbf{k}\tilde{q}(\mathbf{k}) d^3k$$

and with this vector write

$$\dot{\boldsymbol{\sigma}} = [\boldsymbol{\sigma} \times \mathbf{F}] \qquad (2')$$

We write $\boldsymbol{\sigma}$ and $\tilde{q}$ as

$$\boldsymbol{\sigma} = \sum_{\nu} \boldsymbol{\sigma}_{\nu} e^{-i\nu t}$$

$$\tilde{q}(\mathbf{k}) = \sum_{\nu} \tilde{q}_{\nu} e^{-i\nu t}$$

where ν can assume the values 0, $+\omega$, $-\omega$. Substituting into Equation (1), we have

$$\sum_{\nu} (k_0{}^2 - \nu^2) \tilde{q}_{\nu} e^{-i\nu t} = \sum_{\nu} \frac{if}{\pi\sqrt{2}} G(\mathbf{k}) (\boldsymbol{\sigma}_{\nu} \cdot \mathbf{k}) e^{-i\nu t}$$

$$\tilde{q}_{\nu}(\mathbf{k}) = \frac{if}{\pi\sqrt{2}} \frac{G(\mathbf{k})}{k_0{}^2 - \nu^2} (\boldsymbol{\sigma}_{\nu} \cdot \mathbf{k})$$

Writing then

$$\mathbf{F} = \sum_{\nu} \mathbf{F}_{\nu} e^{-i\nu t}$$

we have

$$\mathbf{F}_{\nu} = \frac{f^2}{\pi^2} \int \mathbf{k} \frac{G(\mathbf{k})}{k_0{}^2 - \nu^2} (\boldsymbol{\sigma}_{\nu} \cdot \mathbf{k}) \, d^3k$$

If $G(\mathbf{k})$ depends only on $|\mathbf{k}| = k$, not on the direction of $\mathbf{k}$, we have

$$\mathbf{F}_{\nu} = \boldsymbol{\sigma}_{\nu} \frac{2}{3} f^2 \frac{2}{\pi} \int_0^{\infty} G(k) \frac{k^4}{k_0{}^2 - \nu^2} dk$$

The isotropy of $G(\mathbf{k})$ means spherical symmetry of $U(\mathbf{x})$. The factor $k^4/(k_0{}^2 - \nu^2) = k^4/(k^2 + \mu^2 - \nu^2)$ is broken up into one part, which would converge for G = const., and two parts which would diverge:

$$\frac{k^4}{k^2 + \mu^2 - \nu^2} \equiv k^2 - (\mu^2 - \nu^2) + \frac{(\mu^2 - \nu^2)^2}{k^2 + \mu^2 - \nu^2}$$

At this point the two new mechanical constants are introduced as

$$\frac{2}{\pi}\int_0^\infty G(k)k^2dk = N; \qquad \frac{2}{\pi}\int_0^\infty G(k)dk = \frac{1}{a}$$

In the convergent part, G is approximated by one, the value it would have in the case of a point source.

It is important that due to our generalization, according to which $G(k)$ is not necessarily positive, both a large and a small value of $1/a$ are compatible with the mentioned approximation for the convergent part of the integrals. The particular choice $G(k) = \cos \lambda_0 k_0$, which according to Wentzel and Dirac leads to relativistic invariant results in the limit $\lambda_0 \to 0$, gives in this limit simply $1/a = 0$.[11] In the following we shall not fix the value of $1/a$ by a priori theoretical consideration, but we shall always substitute 1 for $G(k)$ in convergent integrals over k.

There are two cases to be considered: $\mu^2 \gtrless \nu^2$. If $\mu^2 > \nu^2$, the path of integration is the real axis and we have simply

$$\frac{2}{\pi}\int_0^\infty G(k)\,\frac{(\mu^2 - \nu^2)^2dk}{k^2 + (\mu^2 - \nu^2)} \cong \frac{2}{\pi}\int_0^\infty \frac{(\mu^2 - \nu^2)^2dk}{k^2 + (\mu^2 - \nu^2)} = \frac{1}{\sqrt{\mu^2 - \nu^2}}$$

[11] See page 39. Compare W. Pauli, *Phys. Rev.*, **64,** 332 (1943)

In the other case, $\nu^2 > \mu^2$, the path of integration has to be chosen such that the solution obtained represents outgoing waves only. The path of integration, of course, can always be extended to a path from $-\infty$ to $+\infty$. Then by investigating the solution in coordinate space, it can be shown that for $\nu > 0$ the path C must be chosen to obtain outgoing waves only and positive damping of the spin precession. For $\nu < 0$ the complex conjugate of C has to be chosen.

With the paths thus chosen, it can be shown that

$$\frac{1}{\pi}\int_C \frac{dk}{k^2 + (\mu^2 - \nu^2)} = \frac{\pm i}{\sqrt{\nu^2 - \mu^2}} \quad \text{for } \nu \gtrless 0$$

Collecting the foregoing results and definitions, we find for $\mathbf{F}_\nu$ in the two cases:

Case I: $\omega^2 > \mu^2$

$$\mathbf{F}_\nu = \boldsymbol{\sigma}_\nu \cdot \tfrac{2}{3} f^2 [N + (1/a)(\nu^2 - \mu^2) \pm i(\nu^2 - \mu^2)^{3/2}] \quad \text{for } \nu = \pm \omega$$

$$\mathbf{F}_0 = \boldsymbol{\sigma}_0 \cdot \frac{2}{3} f^2 \left[N - \frac{\mu^2}{a} + \mu^3 \right]$$

$$\mathbf{F} = \sum_\nu \mathbf{F}_\nu e^{-i\nu t}$$

$$= \frac{2}{3} f^2 \left\{ \boldsymbol{\sigma}_\omega e^{-i\omega t} \left[N + \frac{\omega^2 - \mu^2}{a} + i(\omega^2 - \mu^2)^{3/2} \right] + \boldsymbol{\sigma}_{-\omega} e^{+i\omega t} \left[N + \frac{\omega^2 - \mu^2}{a} - i(\omega^2 - \mu^2)^{3/2} \right] + \boldsymbol{\sigma}_0 \left[N - \frac{\mu^2}{a} + \mu^3 \right] \right\}$$

$$= \frac{2}{3} f^2 \left\{ \left(N - \frac{\mu^2}{a} + \mu^3 \right) \boldsymbol{\sigma} - \frac{\ddot{\boldsymbol{\sigma}}}{a} + [i(\omega^2 - \mu^2)^{3/2} - \mu^3] \times \right.$$

$$\boldsymbol{\sigma}_\omega e^{-i\omega t} + [-i(\omega^2 - \mu^2)^{3/2} - \mu^3]\boldsymbol{\sigma}_{-\omega} e^{+i\omega t}\Big\}$$

Case II: $\nu^2 < \mu^2$

$$\mathbf{F}_\nu = \boldsymbol{\sigma}_\nu \frac{2}{3} f^2 \{N + (1/a)(\nu^2 - \mu^2) + (\mu^2 - \nu^2)^{3/2}\}$$

The formula for **F** can be written for both cases as

$$\mathbf{F} = \sum \mathbf{F}_\nu e^{-i\nu t} = \frac{2}{3} f^2 \left\{ \left(N - \frac{\mu^2}{a} + \mu^3 \right) \boldsymbol{\sigma} - \frac{1}{a} \ddot{\boldsymbol{\sigma}} + \sum_\nu \left[|\mu^2 - \nu^2|^{3/2} \cdot \epsilon - \mu^3 \right] \boldsymbol{\sigma}_\nu \, e^{-i\nu t} \right\}$$

where $\epsilon = 1$ for $\nu^2 < \mu^2$, $\epsilon = i$ for $\nu > \mu$, $\epsilon = -i$ for $\nu < -\mu$. It should be noted that the first term in both cases—and therefore the constant N—is irrelevant, since it does not affect the equation of motion (2′). The justification for calling the constant $1/a$ "spin inertia" is now found in the fact that it appears as the factor of $\ddot{\boldsymbol{\sigma}}$. If an incident wave is present it will give rise to an additional term in the **F** given below.

To solve the equation of motion (2′) for *case II*, we try the "ansatz"

$$\boldsymbol{\sigma} = [\sqrt{1 - C^2} \cos \omega t, \sqrt{1 - C^2} \sin \omega t, C]$$

with $C^2 < 1$, $\omega^2 < \mu^2$. Expanding in the form $\boldsymbol{\sigma} = \sum_\nu \boldsymbol{\sigma}_\nu e^{-i\nu t}$, we obtain:

$$\boldsymbol{\sigma}_0 = [0, 0, C]$$

$$\boldsymbol{\sigma}_\omega = \left[\frac{1}{2}\sqrt{1 - C^2}, \frac{i}{2}\sqrt{1 - C^2}, 0\right]$$

$$\boldsymbol{\sigma}_{-\omega} = \left[\frac{1}{2}\sqrt{1 - C^2}, -\frac{i}{2}\sqrt{1 - C^2}, 0\right]$$

From (2′), $\dot{\boldsymbol{\sigma}} = [\boldsymbol{\sigma} \times \mathbf{F}]$, follows

$$\frac{d}{dt}(\boldsymbol{\sigma}_0) = 0 = [\boldsymbol{\sigma}_0 \times \mathbf{F}_0]$$

$$e^{i\omega t}\frac{d}{dt}(\boldsymbol{\sigma}_\omega e^{-i\omega t}) = -i\omega\boldsymbol{\sigma}_\omega = [\boldsymbol{\sigma}_\omega \times \mathbf{F}_0] + [\boldsymbol{\sigma}_0 \times \mathbf{F}_\omega]$$

$$e^{-i\omega t}\frac{d}{dt}(\boldsymbol{\sigma}_{-\omega} e^{i\omega t}) = +i\omega\boldsymbol{\sigma}_{-\omega} = [\boldsymbol{\sigma}_{-\omega} \times \mathbf{F}_0] + [\boldsymbol{\sigma}_0 \times \mathbf{F}_{-\omega}]$$

Substituting the above values for $\mathbf{F}_\nu$ we have

$$\boldsymbol{\sigma}_0 \times \mathbf{F}_0 = 0, \text{ because } \mathbf{F}_0 \text{ is parallel to } \boldsymbol{\sigma}_0$$

so the first equation is satisfied. Further

$$[\boldsymbol{\sigma}_\omega \times \mathbf{F}_0] = [\boldsymbol{\sigma}_\omega \times \boldsymbol{\sigma}_0]\cdot\frac{2}{3}f^2\left\{N - \frac{\mu^2}{a} + \mu^3\right\}$$

$$[\boldsymbol{\sigma}_0 \times \mathbf{F}_\omega] = -[\boldsymbol{\sigma}_\omega \times \boldsymbol{\sigma}_0]\cdot\frac{2}{3}f^2\left\{N + \frac{\omega^2 - \mu^2}{a} + (\mu^2 - \omega^2)^{3/2}\right\}$$

$$-i\omega\boldsymbol{\sigma}_\omega = [\boldsymbol{\sigma}_\omega \times \boldsymbol{\sigma}_0]\cdot\frac{2}{3}f^2\left\{-\frac{\omega^2}{a} + \mu^3 - (\mu^2 - \omega^2)^{3/2}\right\}$$

$$-i\omega\begin{pmatrix}\frac{1}{2}\sqrt{1 - C^2}\\ \frac{i}{2}\sqrt{1 - C^2}\\ 0\end{pmatrix} = \begin{pmatrix}\frac{iC}{2}\sqrt{1 - C^2}\\ -\frac{C}{2}\sqrt{1 - C^2}\\ 0\end{pmatrix}\times$$

$$\frac{2}{3}f^2\left\{-\frac{\omega^2}{a} + \mu^3 - (\mu^2 - \omega^2)^{3/2}\right\}$$

Both components yield:

$$\omega = C\cdot\frac{2}{3}f^2\left\{+\frac{\omega^2}{a} - \mu^3 + (\mu^2 - \omega^2)^{3/2}\right\}$$

The equation

$$i\omega\boldsymbol{\sigma}_{-\omega} = [\boldsymbol{\sigma}_{-\omega} \times \mathbf{F}_0] + [\boldsymbol{\sigma}_0 \times \mathbf{F}_{-\omega}]$$

is satisfied by the same value of ω.

This is a complete solution of (2′), since one can show that higher harmonics in $\boldsymbol{\sigma}$ are not excited; with a more general "ansatz" we would find

$$\boldsymbol{\sigma}_{2\omega} = [\boldsymbol{\sigma}_{2\omega} \times \mathbf{F}_0] + [\boldsymbol{\sigma}_\omega \times \mathbf{F}_\omega] + [\boldsymbol{\sigma}_0 \times \mathbf{F}_{2\omega}]$$

but $[\boldsymbol{\sigma}_\omega \times \mathbf{F}_\omega]$ vanishes since $\mathbf{F}_\omega \parallel \boldsymbol{\sigma}_\omega$, and $\mathbf{F}_{2\omega}$ is proportional to $\boldsymbol{\sigma}_{2\omega}$. Thus, we can satisfy this equation by $\boldsymbol{\sigma}_{2\omega} = 0$, i.e., by the original "ansatz."

Considering now the equation for ω, we see that there is always the static solution $\omega = 0$, $C = 1$. This solution means that the angular momentum of the system consisting of nucleon and meson field is carried by the nucleon itself.

The interesting question is whether there are other solutions with $\omega \neq 0$, $C < 1$ describing "stable isobars," i.e., states of higher spin, whose energy is still sufficiently low, so that the system is stable against the actual creation of a meson. Both the case of high and low spin inertia—strong and weak coupling—will be investigated. For these investigations we need the expressions for the energy and the angular momentum of the whole system. It can be shown that the latter has the direction of the x_3-axis and the magnitude

$$L_3 = \frac{1}{3} f^2\omega(1 - C^2)\left\{\frac{1}{a} - \frac{3}{2}(\mu^2 - \omega^2)^{1/2}\right\} + \frac{1}{2} C$$

where the first term represents the angular momentum of the meson field and the second term that of the nucleon.

The energy can be shown to be

$$E = E_0 + \frac{f^2}{6}(1 - C^2)\left\{\frac{\omega^2}{a} + \mu^2 - (\mu^2 - \omega^2)^{3/2} - 3\omega^2(\mu^2 - \omega^2)^{1/2}\right\}$$

where E_0 is the energy of the static solution ($\omega = 0$, $C = 1$).

Case I: $(1/a) \gg \mu$, Strong Coupling Case

In this case we can neglect all but the first term on the right-hand side of the equation

$$\omega = C \cdot \frac{2}{3} f^2 \left\{\frac{\omega^2}{a} - [\mu^3 - (\mu^2 - \omega^2)^{3/2}]\right\}$$

and obtain

$$\omega = \frac{3}{2f^2}\frac{a}{C}$$

Substituting this value in L we have—neglecting $(\mu^2 - \omega^2)^{1/2}$ against $1/a$—

$$L = \frac{1 - C^2}{2C} + \frac{C}{2} = \frac{1}{2C}$$

Now ω and E can be expressed in terms of L:

$$\omega = (3a/f^2)L$$

$$E = (3a/2f^2)L^2 + \text{const.}$$

We note that the relation $\omega = dE/dL$ is verified.

Since $C^2 < 1$, we have $L = 1/2C > \frac{1}{2}$. From the expression for ω, therefore, follows

$$\omega > (3a/2f^2)$$

On the other hand we had previously assumed that $\omega < \mu$. Thus, it follows that

$$(3a/2f^2) < \mu$$

This inequality may also be written as

$$(f\mu)^2 > \frac{3}{2} a\mu$$

If one chooses a of the order of the Compton wavelength of the nucleon, which is in accordance with the above assumption $a\mu \ll 1$, this inequality can be fulfilled in accordance with the known nuclear forces (see following lectures) and we conclude that "stable isobars" exist in the strong coupling case. If, specially, $3a/2f^2$ is not only smaller than, but very small in comparison with μ, there are many stable states of the system. In that case we may expect agreement between the results of quantum theory and the classical theory shown here,[12] if we replace L^2 by $j(j + 1)$. The quantum number j assumes half-integer values starting with $\frac{1}{2}$ and limited from above by the condition that the energy of the system must be smaller than μ. The excitation energy of the lowest isobar state in the theory as considered here is of the order 45 Mev, if one takes for a the Compton wavelength of the proton and $(f\mu)^2 \sim 1$.

Case II: $(1/a) \lesssim \mu$, Including $(1/a) = 0$

This is the case of weak coupling in which perturbation theory can be applied with satisfactory results.

[12] J. R. Oppenheimer and J. Schwinger, *Phys. Rev.*, **60,** 150 (1941). S. M. Dancoff and W. Pauli, *ibid.*, **62,** 85 (1942).

With $x = \omega/\mu$, the equation for ω becomes—neglecting the first term on the right-hand side—

$$-1 = \frac{2}{3}(f\mu)^2 C\gamma(x)$$

where

$$\gamma(x) = \frac{1 - (1 - x^2)^{3/2}}{x}$$

Again we ask whether there is a stable solution, i.e., one with $0 < x < 1$. Since $|C| < 1$, we have the condition

$$\gamma(x) \cdot \frac{2}{3}(f\mu)^2 > 1$$

Since $\gamma(x) \leqq 1.02$, it follows that in order to have stable isobars in the weak coupling case, one needs $\frac{2}{3}(f\mu)^2 > 0.98$. $(f\mu)^2$ is, however, of order $\frac{1}{10}$, and, therefore, stable isobars are impossible in the weak coupling case.

CHAPTER III

Scattering of Mesons

We shall treat the scattering of mesons by nucleons by erecting the same model as that used for the treatment of the stable isobars in the previous lecture, i.e., with pseudoscalar neutral meson field, using classical wave fields and classical equations of motion for the spin of the nucleon. The vector-field theory of scattering has been carried out by Bhabha[13]; and the gyration of the isotopic spin has been treated by Fierz[14] and by Ivanenko and Sokolov.[15]

The formalism has been developed before to a certain stage. On page 18 (*case I*, $\omega > \mu$) an expression for **F** was derived, which, when substituted in the equations of motion

$$\dot{\boldsymbol{\sigma}} = [\boldsymbol{\sigma} \times \mathbf{F}]$$

leads to a damped gyration of $\boldsymbol{\sigma}$, corresponding to the emission of mesons. By introducing an incident meson wave this solution can be made stationary. The process described in this way is a forced gyration of the nucleon spin, which radiates mesons—in other words, scattering of mesons.

The incident wave is described by a propagation

[13] H. J. Bhabha, *Proc. Roy. Soc. London*, **A178,** 314 (1941).

[14] M. Fierz, *Helv. Phys. Acta*, **14,** 257 (1941).

[15] D. Ivanenko and A. Sokolov, *J. Phys. U.S.S.R.*, **3,** 57 (1940).

vector $\mathbf{k}_i$, in the direction of the unit vector $\mathbf{n}_i$ and the amplitude $\mathcal{A}$

$$\phi_i(\mathbf{x}) = \mathcal{A} e^{iK(\mathbf{n}_i \cdot \mathbf{x}) - i\omega t} + \text{complex conjugate}$$

with

$$\mathbf{k}_i = K\mathbf{n}_i$$

where now $\omega > \mu$ and $K^2 = \omega^2 - \mu^2$. In momentum space we have

$$q_i(\mathbf{k}) = \delta(\mathbf{k} - K\mathbf{n}_i)\,\mathcal{A}\,(2\pi)^{3/2} e^{-i\omega t} + \text{complex conjugate}$$

The abbreviation $\mathbf{F}$ occurring in the equations of motion was defined as

$$\mathbf{F} = -\frac{i\sqrt{2}}{\pi} f \int \mathbf{k}\tilde{q}(\mathbf{k}) d^3k$$

where $\tilde{q}(\mathbf{k})$ is now the sum of the former value of $\tilde{q}(\mathbf{k})$ and the incident amplitude

$$\tilde{q}_i(\mathbf{k}) = q_i(\mathbf{k}) \cdot v(-\mathbf{k}) = \delta(\mathbf{k} - K\mathbf{n}_i)\,Ae^{-i\omega t} + \text{complex conjugate with } A = \mathcal{A}(2\pi)^{3/2} v(-\mathbf{k})$$

Therefore $\mathbf{F}$ is expressed by

$$\mathbf{F} = \mathbf{F}_i + \frac{2}{3} f^2 \left\{ -\frac{1}{a}\ddot{\boldsymbol{\sigma}} + (iK^3 - \mu^3)\boldsymbol{\sigma}_\omega e^{-i\omega t} + (-iK - \mu^3)\boldsymbol{\sigma}_{-\omega} e^{i\omega t} \right\}$$

where

$$\mathbf{F}_i = -\frac{\sqrt{2}\,if}{\pi} K\mathbf{n}_i A e^{-i\omega t} + \text{complex conjugate}$$

The second term was derived in Chapter II (page 18, *case I*) but we have now omitted the term proportional to σ, since it does not affect the equations of motion. These are:

$$\dot{\boldsymbol{\sigma}} = \left[\boldsymbol{\sigma} \times \left\{\mathbf{F}_i + \frac{2}{3}f^2\left(-\frac{\ddot{\boldsymbol{\sigma}}}{a} + (iK^3 - \mu^3)\boldsymbol{\sigma}_\omega e^{-i\omega t} - (iK^3 + \mu^3)\boldsymbol{\sigma}_{-\omega}e^{i\omega t}\right)\right\}\right]$$

We shall simplify these equations of motion by considering only terms linear in A in $\sigma_{\pm\omega}$, i.e., by assuming the precession of $\boldsymbol{\sigma}$ caused by the incoming wave small compared to its stationary value. We thus neglect terms of the form $[\boldsymbol{\sigma}_\omega \times \mathbf{F}_i]$ and $[\boldsymbol{\sigma}_\omega \times \boldsymbol{\sigma}_{-\omega}]$. Consistent with these neglections, we take $\dot{\boldsymbol{\sigma}}_\omega = -i\omega\boldsymbol{\sigma}_\omega$ and $\ddot{\boldsymbol{\sigma}}_\omega = -\omega^2\boldsymbol{\sigma}_\omega$ and complex conjugate

$$-i\omega\boldsymbol{\sigma}_\omega e^{-i\omega t} + i\omega\boldsymbol{\sigma}_{-\omega}e^{+i\omega t} = [\boldsymbol{\sigma}_0 \times \mathbf{F}_i] + \left[\boldsymbol{\sigma}_0 \times \frac{2}{3}f^2\left\{\left(iK^3 - \mu^3 + \frac{\omega^2}{a}\right)\boldsymbol{\sigma}_\omega e^{-i\omega t} - \left(iK^3 + \mu^3 - \frac{\omega^2}{a}\right)\boldsymbol{\sigma}_{-\omega}e^{i\omega t}\right\}\right]$$

or

$$-i\omega\boldsymbol{\sigma}_\omega = -\frac{\sqrt{2}\,if}{\pi}KA[\boldsymbol{\sigma}_0 \times \mathbf{n}_i] + \frac{2}{3}f^2\left(iK^3 - \mu^3 + \frac{\omega^2}{a}\right)\left[\boldsymbol{\sigma}_0 \times \boldsymbol{\sigma}_\omega\right]$$

and the complex conjugate equation for $\boldsymbol{\sigma}_{-\omega}$. These are now linear equations for the components of $\boldsymbol{\sigma}_\omega$, and when solved yield the value of $\boldsymbol{\sigma}_\omega$ correct to terms linear in A. The usual perturbation theory would be an expansion in powers of f and up to the term linear in f only. The above theory is more like a dispersion theory.

With $\boldsymbol{\sigma}_\omega$ obtained from the preceding equations, the amplitude A_{sc} of $\phi(\mathbf{x})$ scattered in the direction $\mathbf{n}_s$ can be expressed by

$$A_{sc}^{\pm\omega} = (\mathbf{B}_{\pm\omega} \cdot \mathbf{n}_s)$$

where

$$\mathbf{B} = (2\pi)^{-3/2} i f \pi \sqrt{2} K \boldsymbol{\sigma}_\omega v(K)$$

as derived in the Appendix.

Rather than solving for $\boldsymbol{\sigma}_\omega$, we shall immediately solve for **B**. We get the equation for **B** by multiplying the equation for $\boldsymbol{\sigma}_\omega$ by $-(2\pi)^{-3/2} f\pi\sqrt{2}\, K\omega^{-1} v(K)$

$$\mathbf{B} = \beta\,(\boldsymbol{\sigma}_0 \times \mathbf{n}_i) - iR(\mathbf{B} \times \boldsymbol{\sigma}_0)$$

where

$$R = \frac{2}{3} f^2 \cdot \frac{1}{\omega}\left\{\frac{\omega^2}{a} + iK^3 - \mu^3\right\}$$

and

$$\beta = \frac{2if^2}{\omega}\, \mathfrak{a}\, K^2\, G(K)$$

Obviously **B** is orthogonal to $\boldsymbol{\sigma}_0$, and can therefore be expressed by

$$\mathbf{B} = \gamma[\boldsymbol{\sigma}_0 \times \mathbf{n}_i] + \delta[\boldsymbol{\sigma}_0 \times (\boldsymbol{\sigma}_0 \times \mathbf{n}_i)]$$

which makes the above equation

$$\gamma[\boldsymbol{\sigma}_0 \times \mathbf{n}_i] + \delta[\boldsymbol{\sigma}_0 \times (\boldsymbol{\sigma}_0 \times \mathbf{n}_i)] = \beta[\boldsymbol{\sigma}_0 \times \mathbf{n}_i] + iR\gamma[\boldsymbol{\sigma}_0 \times (\boldsymbol{\sigma}_0 \times \mathbf{n}_i)] - iR\delta[\boldsymbol{\sigma}_0 \times \mathbf{n}_i]$$

or

$$\gamma = \beta - iR\delta$$

$$\delta = iR\gamma$$

and

$$\delta = \frac{iR}{1 - R^2}\,\beta$$

$$\gamma = \beta\,\frac{1}{1 - R^2}$$

$$\mathbf{B} = \frac{2if^2}{\omega}\,\frac{K^2\mathfrak{A}}{1 - R^2}\left\{[\boldsymbol{\sigma}_0 \times \mathbf{n}_i] + iR[\boldsymbol{\sigma}_0 \times (\boldsymbol{\sigma}_0 \times \mathbf{n}_i)]\right\}G(K)$$

$$(\mathbf{B}\cdot\mathbf{B}^*) = \frac{4f^4K^4}{\omega^2}\,|\mathfrak{A}|^2\,\frac{1 + |R|^2}{|1 - R^2|^2}\,\sin^2\alpha\,[G(K)]^2 .$$

where α is the angle between $\mathbf{n}_i$ and $\boldsymbol{\sigma}_0$. The cross section for a scattering into any direction $\mathbf{n}_s$, with the angle α between $\mathbf{n}_i$ and $\boldsymbol{\sigma}_0$ fixed, is

$$Q_\alpha = 4\pi\,\frac{\overline{|A_{\rm sc}|^2}}{|\mathfrak{A}|^2}$$

with the bar denoting averaging over all directions $\mathbf{n}_s$

$$\overline{|A_{\rm sc}|^2} = \overline{(\mathbf{B}\cdot\mathbf{n}_s)\,(\mathbf{B}^*\cdot\mathbf{n}_s)} = \frac{1}{3}(\mathbf{B}\cdot\mathbf{B}^*)$$

By averaging further over all directions $\boldsymbol{\sigma}_0$, the total cross section Q is obtained as

$$Q = \frac{4\pi}{3}\,\frac{(\mathbf{B}\cdot\mathbf{B}^*)_{av}}{|\mathfrak{A}|^2}$$

$$Q = \frac{4\pi}{3}\cdot\frac{4f^4K^4}{\omega^2}\,\frac{1 + |R|^2}{|1 - R^2|^2}\cdot\frac{2}{3}\,[G(K)]^2$$

or

$$\frac{Q}{4\pi} = \frac{8}{9}f^4\,\frac{K^4}{\omega^2}\,\frac{1 + \xi^2 + \eta^2}{(1 - \xi^2 - \eta^2)^2 + 4\eta^2}[G(K)]^2$$

with the abbreviation

$$R = \xi + i\eta$$

$$\xi = \frac{2}{3} f^2 \frac{1}{\omega} \left\{ \frac{\omega^2}{a} - \mu^3 \right\}$$

$$\eta = \frac{2}{3} f^2 \frac{1}{\omega} K^3$$

We shall discuss this result in several limiting cases.

Case I: Strong Coupling, and Energy of the Incident Meson Not Too Large

We assume that $(1/a) \gg \mu$. The condition on the energy is $K^3 \ll (\omega^2/a)$. This condition is certainly fulfilled if $\omega \ll (1/a)$, because then $\omega^3 \ll (\omega^2/a)$ and by definition $K < \omega$. Then η can be neglected compared to ξ, and—because of $\mu < \omega$—the second term in ξ can be neglected. Moreover, $G(K) \sim 1$ for $\omega \ll (1/a)$. In this case, therefore

$$\frac{Q}{4\pi} = \frac{8}{9} f^4 \frac{K^4}{\omega^2} \left[\frac{1 + (\frac{2}{3} f^2 \, \omega/a)^2}{\left(1 - (\frac{2}{3} f^2 \, \omega/a)^2\right)^2} \right]$$

In the usual perturbation theory the term in square brackets would be replaced by unity. If, in addition, the condition for the existence of many stable isobars $(f^2\mu/a) \gg 1$ ("strong coupling") is fulfilled, we may neglect unity against $(\frac{2}{3} f^2\omega/a)^2$ and obtain

$$\frac{Q}{4\pi} = 2 \frac{K^4}{\omega^4} a^2$$

It is noteworthy that f does not appear in this expression. For large energies—provided they do not violate the condition $K^3 \ll (\omega^2/a)$—we have

$$(Q/4\pi) \sim 2a^2$$

Case II: $(1/a) < \mu$, Including Especially $(1/a) = 0$ and $\eta \gg \xi$.

We again put $G(K) \sim 1$. The latter condition is fulfilled if K is large in comparison with both $1/a$ and μ. Neglecting ξ results in

$$\frac{Q}{4\pi} = \frac{8}{9} f^4 \frac{K^4}{\omega^2} \frac{1}{1+\eta^2}$$

$$= \frac{2}{K^2} \frac{\left(\frac{2}{3} f^2 K^3/\omega\right)^2}{1 + \left(\frac{2}{3} f^2 K^3/\omega\right)^2}$$

If, in addition, $K \gg 10\mu$, this result simplifies to

$$Q/4\pi = 2/K^2$$

since $(f\mu)^2$ is of the order $\frac{1}{10}$.

Bhabha[16] has carried through a classical calculation for the transverse vector–meson field. We may write Bhabha's formula (82),[17] for the total cross section of a transverse meson as

$$6\pi \sin^2\theta \frac{(\omega_0{}^2 - \chi^2)^2}{\omega_0{}^2} \frac{1}{\alpha^2} \frac{1 + (\xi/\alpha)^2 + (\zeta/\alpha)^2}{[1 - (\xi/\alpha)^2 - (\zeta/\alpha)^2]^2 + 4(\zeta/\alpha)^2}$$

where $\alpha = \frac{3}{2} I/g_2{}^2$, and θ is the angle between the polarization of the incident meson and the spin of the nucleon.

$$\frac{\xi}{\alpha} = \frac{K\omega_0}{I} - \frac{2}{3}\frac{g_2{}^2\chi^3}{I\omega_0} = \frac{2}{3}\frac{g_2{}^2}{I\omega_0}\left[\frac{3}{2}\frac{K\omega_0{}^2}{g_2{}^2} - \chi^3\right]$$

$$\frac{\zeta}{\alpha} = \frac{2}{3}\frac{g_2{}^2}{I}\frac{(\omega_0{}^2 - \chi^2)^{3/2}}{\omega_0}$$

[16] H. J. Bhabha, *Proc. Roy. Soc. London*, **A178,** 314 (1941).
[17] *Ibid.*, p. 337.

By definition we should set in parallel the following quantities:

Pauli	Bhabha
μ	χ
ω	ω_0
$K = \sqrt{\omega^2 - \mu^2}$	$\sqrt{\omega_0{}^2 - \chi^2}$

K and I, in Bhabha's paper, are arbitrary constants of the dimension of an angular momentum. We can, therefore, determine K such that $\frac{3}{2}\, K/g_2{}^2$ corresponds to Pauli's $1/a$. Bhabha's expression in this notation, takes the form

$$6\pi \sin^2\theta \, \frac{K^4}{\omega^2}\left(\frac{2}{3}\frac{g_2{}^2}{I}\right)^2 \frac{1 + (\xi/\alpha)^2 + (\zeta/\alpha)^2}{[1 - (\xi/\alpha)^2 - (\zeta/\alpha)^2]^2 + 4\,(\zeta/\alpha)^2}$$

where

$$\frac{\xi}{\alpha} = \frac{2}{3}\frac{g_2{}^2}{I\omega}\left[\frac{\omega^2}{a} - \mu^3\right]$$

$$\frac{\zeta}{\alpha} = \frac{2}{3}\frac{g_2{}^2}{I}\frac{K^3}{\omega}$$

We get complete correspondence by determining I such as to have $g_2{}^2/I = f^2$. Then ξ/α becomes ξ and ζ/α becomes η and we have

$$(Q_\theta)_{\text{Bhabha}} = \frac{8}{3}\pi \sin^2\theta \, \frac{f^4K^4}{\omega^2} \, \frac{1 + \xi^2 + \eta^2}{[1 - \xi^2 - \eta^2]^2 + 4\,\eta^2}$$

for transverse mesons, which is less, just by a factor 2, than the result derived above,

$$Q_\alpha = \frac{4\pi}{3}\frac{(\mathbf{B}\cdot\mathbf{B}^*)}{|\mathfrak{a}|^2}$$

for neutral pseudoscalar mesons, where α is the angle between the direction of incidence of the mesons and the spin of the nucleon. The curves computed by

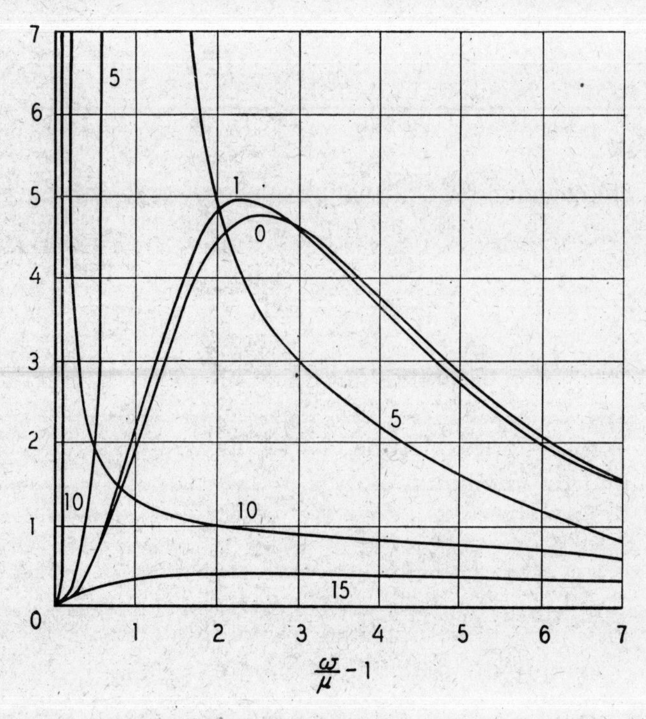

FIGURE 1

Cross section for scattering in units: $(6\pi \sin^2 \theta)/(100\ \mu^2)$, for transverse vector mesons (Bhabha); $(12\pi \sin^2 \alpha)/(100\ \mu^2)$, for pseudoscalar neutral mesons (Pauli). (The parameters are the values of $1/a\mu$ from 0 to 15.)

Bhabha can be used for our case too, and are shown in Figure 1 with the present notation. Bhabha's computation is based on the values

$$\mu = 4.42 \times 10^{12} \text{ cm}^{-1} \text{ corresponding to a meson mass of 170 electron masses}$$

$$(f\mu)^2 = \frac{3}{20}$$

Magnetic Moment in the Strong Coupling Case

$$[(1/a) \gg \mu, f^2\mu \gg a \text{ or } (f\mu)^2 \gg a\mu]$$

The symmetrical pseudoscalar theory has been carried through by Dancoff and Pauli.[18] The interaction energy is

$$H_{\text{int}} = \sqrt{4\pi}\, f \sum_{\alpha=1}^{3} \tau_\alpha \int U(x)(\boldsymbol{\sigma}\cdot\nabla)\varphi_\alpha d^3x$$

In the strong coupling approximation this interaction energy is diagonalized first, and its lowest state is used as zeroth approximation. This means that one has to find the minimum of $\sum_{\alpha k} \tau_\alpha \sigma_k C_{\alpha k}$ where

$$C_{\alpha k} = \sqrt{4\pi}\, f \int U(\mathbf{x}) \frac{\partial \varphi_\alpha}{\partial x_k} d^3x = -\sqrt{4\pi}\, f \int \frac{\partial U}{\partial x_k} \varphi_\alpha d^3x$$

The problem is simplified by the result that a necessary condition for the minimum of

$$E_{\text{pot}} + H_{\text{int}} = \tfrac{1}{2} \sum_\alpha \int \varphi_\alpha (-\Delta + \mu^2)\varphi_\alpha d^3x + \sum_{\alpha,k} \tau_\alpha \sigma_k C_{\alpha k}$$

is given by

$$C_{\alpha k} = C e_{\alpha k} \qquad (3)$$

where the $\mathbf{e}_\alpha$ are a system of three orthogonal vectors in space:

$$(\mathbf{e}_\alpha \cdot \mathbf{e}_\beta) = \delta_{\alpha\beta}$$

[18] S. M. Dancoff and W. Pauli, *Phys. Rev.*, **62,** 85 (1942).

The problem of finding the lowest eigenvalue of $\sum_{\alpha,k} \tau_\alpha \sigma_k e_{\alpha k}$ is simpler than the more general case of the lowest eigenvalue of $\sum_{\alpha,k} \tau_\alpha \sigma_k C_{\alpha k}$. The particular case is, indeed, immediately reduced to the lowest eigenvalue of

$$\sum_{\alpha=1}^{3} \tau_\alpha \sigma_\alpha$$

$$\sigma_\alpha = \sum_k e_{\alpha k} \sigma_k \qquad \sigma_k = \sum_\alpha \sigma_\alpha e_{\alpha k}$$

being a rotation in the spin-space. This rotation being made, the problem of composing the isotopic spin and the ordinary spin is equivalent to the composition of two electron spins. The lowest eigenvalue corresponds to the "singlet state" for which

$$\tau_\alpha + \sigma_\alpha = 0, \text{ hence } \tau_1\sigma_1 = \tau_2\sigma_2 = \tau_3\sigma_3 = -1 \quad (4)$$

Therefore

$$H_{\text{int}} = \sum_{\alpha,k} \tau_\alpha \sigma_k C_{\alpha k} = C \sum_\alpha \tau_\alpha \sigma_\alpha = -3C$$

The "singlet state" defined by (4) is equivalent to the rule that $\tau_\alpha \sigma_k$ can be replaced by $-e_{\alpha k}$, a rule which is very convenient for practical use. The minimum of $E_{\text{pot}} + H_{\text{int}}$ is reached if φ_α satisfies the condition

$$(-\Delta + \mu^2)\varphi_\alpha = -\sqrt{4\pi}\, f(\mathbf{e}_\alpha \nabla) U(\mathbf{x})$$

which is solved by

$$\varphi_\alpha = -\frac{f}{\sqrt{4\pi}} (\mathbf{e}_\alpha \nabla) \chi(x)$$

with

$$\chi(\mathbf{x}) = \int U(\mathbf{x}') \frac{e^{-\mu r}}{r} d^3x', \qquad r = |\,\mathbf{x} - \mathbf{x}'\,|$$

Due to the spherical symmetry of $U(\mathbf{x})$, the assumption (3) is verified by inserting this expression for φ_α into the formula for $C_{\alpha k}$. Moreover one obtains

$$C = f^2 \int \frac{\partial\chi}{\partial x}\frac{\partial U}{\partial x} d^3x = f^2 \frac{1}{3} \int (\nabla\chi)\cdot(\nabla U) d^3x$$

We remark that with the help of the function $G(k)$ defined in Chapter II one can also write in momentum space

$$C = \frac{f^2}{3}\cdot\frac{2}{\pi}\int_0^\infty G(k)\,\frac{k^4}{k^2+\mu^2}\,dk$$

One finds easily $E_{\text{pot}} = -\frac{1}{2} E_{\text{int}}$; hence, for the total self-energy

$$E_0 = E_{\text{pot}} + H_{\text{int}}$$

$$E_0 = -\tfrac{3}{2}\,C$$

The isobar separation E is found to be

$$E = \frac{3a}{f^2}\, j(j+1)$$

where j is the quantum number of the angular momentum. The charge is characterized by the quantum number

$$n = \text{charge} - \tfrac{1}{2}$$

where n is limited by

$$-j \leq n \leq j$$

For $j = \frac{1}{2}$ only proton and neutron are allowed. The charge is formally the component of the angular momentum in a field-fixed direction. The fact that, for given j, E does not depend on n is characteristic for the symmetric theories.

In the "singlet" state of the strong coupling theory the nucleon is as often proton as neutron:

$$\bar{\boldsymbol{\sigma}} = 0$$

$$\bar{\boldsymbol{\tau}} = 0$$

This has the consequence that the magnetic moment has the opposite sign for proton ($\mathfrak{M}_P$) and neutron ($\mathfrak{M}_N$) but the same absolute value:

$$\mathfrak{M}_{PN} = \pm \left(\frac{1}{9}\frac{f^2}{a} M + \frac{1}{6}\right) \text{ proton magnetons}$$

where M is the mass of the proton. The absolute value is reasonable but the opposite sign would give the deuteron the magnetic moment zero (apart from the small contribution of the orbital moment of the proton), in contradiction with experiment. Experimentally it is found that

$$\mathfrak{M}_P = 2.785 \pm 0.02 \text{ proton magnetons}$$

$$\mathfrak{M}_N = -\ 1.935 \pm 0.02 \text{ proton magnetons}$$

Hence $\mathfrak{M}_P + \mathfrak{M}_N = 0.85$.

The general expression for the magnetic moment $\mathfrak{M}$ including the case of isobars, is

$$\mathfrak{M} = \frac{n}{j+1}\left(\frac{1}{3}\frac{f^2}{a} M + \frac{1}{2}\right) \text{ proton magnetons}$$

The g-factor is therefore

$$g = \frac{\mathfrak{M}}{j} = \frac{n}{j(j+1)} \left(\frac{1}{3} \frac{f^2}{a} M + \frac{1}{2} \right)$$

This general expression reduces to the above expression for $\mathfrak{M}_{N,P}$ in the case of proton and neutron where $j = \frac{1}{2}$ and $n = \pm\frac{1}{2}$, and thus $n/(j+1) = \pm\frac{1}{3}$.

The magnetic moment has also a part the expectation value of which is zero for a given isobar, but which has matrix elements corresponding to a transition between isobars of the same electric charge n but of different spin values j. They should give rise to the emission of a photon by magnetic dipole radiation of the higher spin isobars, an effect which is discussed in a paper by Jauch.[19]

Magnetic Moment in the Weak Coupling Case

The weak coupling theories, in both their vector and pseudoscalar forms, lead to the result that $\mathfrak{M}_P = 1 + \mathfrak{M}$, $\mathfrak{M}_N = -\mathfrak{M}$ where

$$\mathfrak{M} = \frac{M}{\mu} \frac{4}{3} (f\mu)^2 C, \quad \text{with } C = \frac{2}{\pi\mu} \int_0^\infty \frac{k^4 G(k)\, dk}{(k^2 + \mu^2)^2}$$

It should be noted that in this case the sum $\mathfrak{M}_P + \mathfrak{M}_N = 1$, in better agreement with experiment.

This expression for C is evaluated in the following manner. We add to and subtract from the numerator $2\mu^2k^2 + \mu^4$, obtaining thus

$$C = \frac{2}{\pi\mu} \int_0^\infty G(k)dk \left[1 - \frac{2\,\mu^2k^2 + \mu^4}{(k^2 + \mu^2)^2} \right]$$

[19] J. M. Jauch, *Phys. Rev.*, **69**, 275 (1946).

$$= \frac{2}{\pi\mu}\int_0^\infty G(k)\,dk - \frac{2}{\pi\mu}\int_0^\infty \frac{(2\mu^2k^2 + \mu^4)\,G(k)\,dk}{(k^2+\mu^2)^2}$$

The first term is $1/\mu a$ by definition. The second integral is convergent, so we replace $G(k)$ by unity and the integration yields the value $\frac{3}{2}$; therefore, $C = (1/\mu a) - \frac{3}{2}$.

In the λ-limiting process of Dirac and Wentzel, a time-like four vector $\lambda = \{\boldsymbol{\lambda}, \lambda_0\}$ is introduced and our function $G(k)$ is defined by $G(\mathbf{k}) = \cos(\boldsymbol{\lambda}\cdot\mathbf{k} - \lambda_0 k_0)$ with $k_0 = \sqrt{k^2+\mu^2}$. If terms of order μ/M are neglected, i.e., if the nucleon is considered infinitely heavy, and, therefore, at rest, the rest system of the nucleon can be used as system of reference for the calculation. The four vector λ is then chosen specially such that its spatial components vanish. In this approximation ($\mu/M \ll 1$), therefore, $G(\mathbf{k})$ can be written as $G(k) = \cos\lambda_0 k_0$, and

$$\int_0^\infty \cos\left(\lambda_0\sqrt{k^2+\mu^2}\right)dk = \int_0^\infty \cos(\lambda_0\mu\cosh t)\,\mu\cosh t\,dt$$

$$= \frac{d}{d\lambda_0}\int_0^\infty \sin(\lambda_0\mu\cosh t)dt = -\frac{\pi\mu}{2}J_1(\lambda_0\mu)$$

The assumption that λ is time-like guarantees that λ_0 is real. In the limit $\lambda_0 \to 0$ we have thus[20]

$$\frac{1}{a} = \lim_{\lambda_0\to 0}\frac{2}{\pi}\int_0^\infty \cos\left(\lambda_0\sqrt{k+\mu^2}\right)dk = \lim_{\lambda_0\to 0}[-\mu J_1(\lambda_0\mu)] = 0$$

This shows that for the special case $1/a = 0$, the theory of the extended source can be carried through in relativistically invariant form. Attempts to do this for the case $1/a \neq 0$ have failed.

[20] J. M Jauch, *Phys. Rev.*, **63**, 335 (1943).

It does not seem, however, that the λ-limiting process is the correct approach, since it leads to a proton magnetic moment of less than one proton magneton and to a positive moment for the neutron. It seems that it would be better to postpone the question of the relativistic invariance of the theory and to choose $1/a$ so that the results are in agreement with experiments.

Assuming the quantity $1/\mu a = 2.85$, the results are in agreement with experiment. This seems a reasonable assumption for it makes the quantity $a \cong \frac{1}{3} \cdot \hbar/\mu c$, i.e., one-third of the Compton wavelength of the meson. The experiments thus favor an intermediate coupling theory. It should be pointed out that the results for the magnetic moment are the same whether one uses a symmetrical or charged theory, since only the charged mesons contribute to the magnetic moment.

CHAPTER IV

Quantum Theory of Scattering

Theory of Radiation Damping

Heitler[21] has given a correspondence scheme which is a generalization of the wave-mechanical theory of line width of Weisskopf and Wigner and by which he can eliminate in a Lorentz invariant manner the divergences occurring in the treatment of scattering processes. This scheme consists in adding a new rule to the existing formalism of quantum mechanics. He hopes to obtain thus an approximate theory which would have the same relation to a future quantum mechanics that Bohr's quantization of classical orbits had to quantum mechanics. This rule is superimposed on the quantum-mechanical theory of scattering processes.

Let H_0 be the Hamiltonian of a free particle and H the interaction energy; the Schrödinger equation can be written as

$$(H_0 + H - E_k)\, \phi_k = 0$$

[21] W. Heitler and H. W. Peng, *Proc. Cambridge Phil. Soc.*, **38,** 296 (1942). Independently, similar proposals were made by: E. Gora, *Z. Physik,* **120,** 121 (1943); A. Sokolov, *J. Phys. U.S.S.R.*, **5,** 231 (1941); and A. H. Wilson, *Proc. Cambridge Phil. Soc.*, **37,** 301 (1941). The stationary solution presented here is due to Gora. It constitutes an important simplification over the damped solution which was used by Heitler, Sokolov, *et al.* The stationary solution was later also used by S. T. Ma, *Proc. Cambridge Phil. Soc.*, **39,** 168 (1943), and S. T. Ma and C. F. Hsueh, *ibid.*, **40,** 167 (1944).

If in particular we consider ϕ_k as the wave function in momentum space, H_0 becomes a constant E_0, the energy of the system without interaction, and we have

$$(E_k - E_0)\,\phi_k = H\,\phi_k$$

The symbol k, thereby, denotes all variables necessary to define a state of the system, *including* the energy. $H\phi_k$ is now expanded in terms of the functions ϕ_k:

$$H\phi_k = \sum_l (k|H|l)\phi_l$$

To include the choice of the incident wave we shall write for ϕ_k the matrix $(k|\phi|0)$ and finally

$$(E_k - E_0)(k|\phi|0) = \sum_l (k|H|l)(l|\phi|0)$$

To solve this Schrödinger equation we shall substitute an ansatz based on Dirac's theory of scattering.[22] Dirac shows there that to have outgoing waves only in coordinate space, the wave function in momentum space must be of the form

$$\phi(\mathbf{p}) = f(p, \mathbf{n})\left[\frac{1}{E - E'} + i\pi\delta(E - E')\right]$$

where $\mathbf{p} = p\mathbf{n}$, f is a regular function, E is the energy belonging to $\mathbf{p}$ and E' the energy of the initial state. In coordinate space, the wave function for large r, with $\mathbf{x} = r\mathbf{n}$, has the form

$$\phi(\mathbf{x}) \sim (2\pi)^{1/2}\,p'\,\frac{dp'}{dE'}\,f(p', \mathbf{n})\,\frac{e^{ip'r}}{r}$$

Accordingly, we introduce the ansatz

[22] P. A. M. Dirac, *Principles of Quantum Mechanics.* Oxford Univ. Press, London, 1935, pp. 197 *et seq.*

$$\phi_k \equiv (k|\phi|0) = \delta_{k0} + (k|f|0)\left[\frac{1}{E_k - E_0} + i\pi\delta\,(E_0 - E_k)\right]$$

where

$$\delta_{k0} = (A|1|0)\delta(E_k - E_0)$$

Italic capitals thereby denote all variables necessary to define the state k, *excluding* the energy. In this notation we have to write

$$(k'|\phi|k'') = (E', A'|\phi|E'', A'')$$

and

$$\sum_k = \int dE \int_A$$

where $\int_A$ means either a sum, or an integral, or both over all states A which have the same energy. All states A of the same energy are said to be on the same "energy shell." In particular the matrix $(A|1|B)$ is defined by

$$\int_B F(B)(A|1|B) = F(A)$$

Inserting the ansatz into the Schrödinger equation, we have an equation to determine $(k|f|0)$:

$$(E_k - E_0)\left\{\delta_{k0} + (k|f|0)\left[\frac{1}{E_k - E_0} + i\pi\delta(E_0 - E_k)\right]\right\} =$$

$$\sum_l (k|H|l)\left\{\delta_{l0} + (l|f|0)\left[\frac{1}{E_l - E_0} + i\pi\delta(E_0 - E_l)\right]\right\}$$

where the summation over l at the singular value $E_l = E_0$ has to be taken in the sense of a principal value. Since $(E_0 - E_k)\,\delta(E_0 - E_k)$ vanishes, we have

$$(k|f|0) = (k|H|0) + \sum_l \frac{(k|H|l)}{E_l - E_0}(l|f|0) + i\pi \int_A (k|H|A)(A|f|0) \quad (5)$$

If, now, we substitute into the sum on the right-hand side of Equation (5) its value as given by this very Equation (5), we obtain

$$(k|f|0) = (k|H|0) + i\pi \int_A (k|H|A)(A|f|0) + \sum_l \frac{(k|H|l)}{E_l - E_0}\left[(l|H|0) + \sum_{l'} \frac{(l|H|l')}{E_{l'} - E_0}(l'|f|0) + i\pi \int (l|H|A)(A|f|0)\right] = (k|H^{(1)}|0) + (k|H^{(2)}|0) + i\pi \int_A (k|H^{(1)}|A)(A|f|0) + i\pi \int_A (k|H^{(2)}|A)(A|f|0) + \sum_{l'} \frac{(k|H^{(2)}|l')}{E_{l'} - E_0}(l'|f|0)$$

where

$$(k|H^{(1)}|l) = (k|H|l); \; (k|H^{(N+1)}|l) = \sum_n \frac{(k|H^{(N)}|n)(n|H|l)}{E_n - E_0}$$

and, therefore,

$$(k|H^{(\nu)}|l) = \sum_{n_1, n_2 \ldots n_{\nu-1}} \frac{(k|H|n_1)(n_1|H|n_2)\ldots(n_{\nu-1}|H|l)}{(E_{n_1} - E_0)(E_{n_2} - E_0)\ldots(E_{n_{\nu-1}} - E_0)}$$

Obviously, by substituting (5) $N - 1$ times into the sum on the right-hand side, we obtain

$$(k|f|0) = \sum_{\nu=1}^{N}\left\{(k|H^{(\nu)}|0) + i\pi \int_A (k|H^{(\nu)}|A)(A|f|0)\right\} + \sum_l \frac{(k|H^{(N)}|l)}{E_l - E_0}(l|f|0)$$

If this iteration process were a convergent procedure i.e., if

$$\lim_{n\to\infty} \sum_l \frac{(k|H^{(n)}|l)}{E_l - E_0} (l|f|0) = 0$$

we would have an integral equation for $(k|f|0)$, which for values of $(k|f|0)$ on the energy shell can be written

$$(A|\underline{f}|0) = (A|\underline{K}|0) + i\pi \textstyle\int_B (A|\underline{K}|B)(B|\underline{f}|0)$$

where

$$(l|K|m) = \sum_{\nu=1}^{\infty} (l|H^{(\nu)}|m)$$

and the "$(A|\underline{K}|B)$" is underlined to indicate that it is a submatrix on the energy shell.

The process leading to this integral equation converges if finite source functions are used to describe the particles, but is divergent for point sources. By the introduction of finite sources, however, one loses the relativistic invariance.

Instead, Heitler introduces as an additional rule that in the sum for $(A|\underline{K}|B)$ all terms beyond the lowest nonvanishing term shall be omitted.

If, e.g., the symbol A denotes a state with one meson present,

$$(E, A|H^{(1)}|E', B) = 0$$

except if B denotes a state with none or two mesons present, provided that H—as usual—is an operator of creation or annihilation of a meson. If B is a state with one meson present, $(A|H^{(1)}|B) = 0$ and $(A|H^{(2)}|B)$ is the first of the matrix-elements $(A|H^{(\nu)}|B)$ which is different from zero. In this case Heitler's rule would prescribe taking only $(A|H^{(2)}|B)$ and omitting all higher $(A|H^{(\nu)}|B)$.

For weak-coupling theories Heitler's procedure must, therefore, give the same results as the usual calculations of the first approximation in a perturbation theory, for which the second approximation diverges.

It can be proved that Heitler's procedure is relativistically invariant. It bears a certain resemblance to the λ-limiting process but is not identical with it. This similarity holds to the extent that in Heitler's theory, too, no new constant with the significance of a spin-inertia appears.

Heisenberg's "Observable Quantities"

The submatrix on the energy shell, which was first used by Wheeler,[23] has been made the subject of a detailed investigation by Heisenberg.[24] The difficulties of the present theory—he points out—may yield some information as to which concepts will be eliminated in the future theory. We may, in fact, expect that concepts which imply the measurement of a point in space-time with unlimited accuracy will not survive. On the other hand, quantities which are directly observable will have to appear in any future theory. These are: (*1*) the discrete energy values of stationary states of closed systems; and (*2*) the asymptotic behavior of wave functions at infinity in collision, emission, and absorption processes.[25]

[23] J. A. Wheeler, *Phys. Rev.*, **52,** 1107 (1937).

[24] W. Heisenberg, *Z. Physik*, **120,** 513, 673 (1943).

[25] This point of view encounters the difficulty that, by the restriction to these observable quantities, one loses the possibility of calculating certain other quantities. For instance, no method is known which determines such quantities as the part of the magnetic proton moment caused by the meson field, using only quantities defined on the energy shell.

In the latter case all the information about the scattering process is contained in a matrix on the energy shell $(A|\underline{S}|B)$ which is connected with the quantities used in the former chapter. The wave function $(k|\phi|0)$ can be divided into an incoming part $(k|\phi_-|0)$ and an outgoing part $(k|\phi_+|0)$, by splitting the incident plane wave into an incoming wave and an outgoing wave. With Heisenberg's notation we have as a factor appearing in the incoming wave function

$$\delta_+(x) = \tfrac{1}{2}\,\delta(x) - (1/2\pi i x)$$

$$\delta_-(x) = \tfrac{1}{2}\,\delta(x) + (1/2\pi i x) = \delta_+^*(\underline{x})$$

We may then write

$$\begin{aligned} \delta_{k0} &= (A|\underline{1}|0)\,\delta(E_0 - E_k) \\ &= (A|\underline{1}|0)\,[\delta_+\,(E_0 - E_k) + \delta_-\,(E_0 - E_k)] \end{aligned}$$

and

$$(k|\phi|0) = (k|\phi^+|0) + (k|\phi^-|0)$$

with

$$(k|\phi^-|0) = (A|\underline{1}|0)\,\delta_-(E_0 - E_k)$$

$$(k|\phi^+|0) = [(A|\underline{1}|0) + 2\pi i(k|f|0)]\delta_+(E_0 - E_k)$$

We are especially interested in the factor of δ_+ in the last equation, when the state k has the same energy as the state 0. This submatrix on the energy shell we shall call

$$(A|\underline{S}|0) = (A|\underline{1}|0) + 2\pi i\,(A|\underline{f}|0)$$

or written in matrix form

$$\underline{S} = 1 + 2\pi i \underline{f}$$

The absolute squares of the matrix elements $(A|\underline{S}|B)$ are in simple scattering processes interpreted as probabilities of finding the scattered particle in a state A at a large distance from the scattering center, when the incoming particle was in the state B. This interpretation is possible if

$$\int_B |(A|\underline{S}|B)|^2 = 1$$

i.e., if $\underline{S}$ is a unitary matrix, because

$$\int_B |(A|\underline{S}|B)|^2 = \int_B (A|\underline{S}|B)(A|\underline{S}|B)^*$$

Denoting by S^+ the Hermitian conjugate of S, defined by $(A|S^+|B) = (B|S|A)^*$, we may write

$$\begin{aligned}\int_B |(A|\underline{S}|B)|^2 &= \int_B (A|\underline{S}|B)(B|\underline{S}^+|A) \\ &= \underline{S}\,\underline{S}^+ = 1 \text{ for unitary } \underline{S}\end{aligned}$$

In order to be able to carry over this interpretation of $(A|\underline{S}|B)$ to processes involving emission and absorption it has to be shown that $(A|\underline{S}|B)$ is unitary. The general proof is based on the Schrödinger equation, assuming thus the existence, still, of a Hamiltonian. In a future theory, Heisenberg believes, there will probably be no longer a Hamiltonian but there will still be a unitary matrix describing the general scattering process.

We shall now give a proof of the theorem of Heisenberg that the matrix $\underline{S}$, introduced on page 47, is a unitary matrix, i.e., $\underline{S}^+\underline{S} = 1$. The proof to be given is one that was developed by Pauli and Bargmann. It is particularly adapted to this case and does not make use of Heitler's integral equation nor of different times as used in the proof given by Heisenberg. We recall that the Schrödinger function representing an incident plane wave and an outgoing scattered wave may be written in momentum space as

$$(k|\phi|0) = (k|1|0) + (k|F|0) \qquad (6a)$$

$$(k|F|0) = (k|f|0)\left[\frac{1}{E_k - E_0} + i\pi\delta\,(E_k - E_0)\right] \qquad (6b)$$

with $(k|f|0)$ regular.

From the definition of $(k|f|0)$ by (6a) and (6b) it follows that

$$(H_0 - E_0)(k|\phi|0) = (k|f|0) \qquad (7)$$

because the operator H_0 in momentum space is merely a multiplication by E_k and, therefore, we have

$$(H_0 - E_0)(k|\phi|0) = (E_k - E_0) \times \left\{(k|1|0) + (k|f|0)\left[\frac{1}{E_k - E_0} + i\pi\delta\,(E_k - E_0)\right]\right\}$$

and—since $(k|1|0) = \delta_{k0} = (A|\underline{1}|0)\delta(E_k - E_0)$ (see page 43)—the first and last terms vanish and we are left with Equation (7).

On the other hand we have the Schrödinger equation

$$(H_0 - E_0)(k|\phi|0) = H\,(k|\phi|0)$$

(see page 42), so that

$$(k|f|0) = H(k|\phi|0)$$

Substituting for $(k|\phi|0)$ from equation (6a), we find

$$(k|f|0) = H\,\{(k|1|0) + (k|F|0)\}$$
$$= (k|H|0) + (k|HF|0)$$

which, in matrix notation, becomes

$$f = H + HF$$

We now write the Hermitian conjugate equation

$$f^+ = H^+ + (HF)^+ = H + F^+H$$

since H is Hermitian, i.e., $H^+ = H$, where

$$(k|F^+|0) = -(k|f^+|0)\left[\frac{1}{E_k - E_0} + i\pi\delta\,(E_0 - E_k)\right]$$

Multiplying f to the left by F^+ and f^+ to the right by F, we have

$$F^+f = F^+H + F^+HF \text{ and } f^+F = HF + F^+\,HF$$

Subtracting these two equations, the terms F^+HF cancel and we have

$$F^+f - f^+F = F^+H - HF$$

But $F^+H - HF = f^+ - f$ and therefore

$$F\,f - f^+F = f^+ - f$$

or

$$f^+ - f + f^+F - F^+f = 0$$

This may be regarded as a generalization of the orthogonality relations. Writing this out in full and making use of the definition of F we have

$$(A,E|f^+ - f|0,E_0) + \int_{A'}\int dE' \frac{(A,E,|f^+|A'E')(A'E'|f|0,E_0)}{E' - E_0}$$

$$+ i\pi \int_{A'} (A,E|f^+|A'E_0)(A',E_0|f|0,E_0)$$

$$+ \int_{A'}\int dE' \frac{(A,E|f^+|A'E')(A'E'|f|0\,E_0)}{E - E'}$$

$$+ i\pi \int_{A'} (AE|f^+|A'E)(A'E|f|0,E_0) = 0$$

This relation holds generally for all values of E and E_0. We now specialize this to states on the same energy shell where $E = E_0$. We find

$$(A|\underline{f}^+ - \underline{f}|0) = -2i\pi \int_{A'} (A|\underline{f}^+|A')(A'|\underline{f}|0)$$

since then the double integrals are equal and cancel, and the single integrals are equal. Therefore as a matrix equation we have

$$\underline{f}^+ - \underline{f} + 2\pi i\, \underline{f}^+\underline{f} = 0$$

Now the matrix $\underline{S}$ was defined as $\underline{1} + 2\pi i\underline{f}$ and, therefore,

$$\underline{S}^+\underline{S} = (1 - 2\pi i\underline{f}^+)(1 + 2\pi i\underline{f}) = 1 - 2\pi i\,[\underline{f}^+ - \underline{f} + 2\pi i\underline{f}^+\,\underline{f}]$$

but it was proved above that the quantity in brackets vanishes and hence $\underline{S}^+\underline{S} = 1$, which was to be proved.

CHAPTER V

Theory of Neutron–Proton Scattering

We now return to a discussion of the theory of neutron–proton scattering. The angular dependence of the neutron–proton scattering for energies in the range from 12 to 20 Mev can give us information about the nature of the forces in the P-states. In particular the sign of the potential in the P-states is opposite in sign to that in the S-states if the force is of an exchange type rather than an ordinary force. Because of the exclusion principle, spin and charge must have different symmetry character for the orbit-symmetrical S-state, but equal symmetry character for the orbit-antisymmetrical P-state. It is therefore easily seen that an exchange of spin, or charge, or space coordinates will result in a different sign of the interaction energy for P- and S-states. Since, for energies in the range mentioned above, the De Broglie wavelength is still much greater than the range of the forces, the scattering into states of higher angular momentum will decrease rapidly as the angular momentum increases.

In the following discussion the influence of the tensor forces on the scattering will be neglected, and only central forces will be considered. The wave function of the scattered neutrons at large distances will be given by $f(\theta) \cdot e^{ikr}/r$ in the center of gravity reference system.

The angular dependence is described[26] by

$$f(\theta) = \frac{1}{2ik} \sum_{l=0}^{\infty} (2l + 1)(e^{2i\delta_l} - 1)P_l(\cos\theta)$$

where l is the quantum number of the orbital angular momentum, and the $P_l(\cos\theta)$ are the Legendre functions. The phase δ_l is defined by the solution corresponding to a given angular momentum, which is regular for small r and behaves for large r as $(1/r)\sin(kr - \frac{1}{2}l\pi + \delta_l)$. If there is no interaction energy the value of δ_l is zero; if the interaction energy is sufficiently small one has approximately[27]

$$\sin\delta_l = -\pi\frac{m}{\hbar^2}\int_0^{\infty} V(r)\,[J_{l+1/2}(kr)]^2 r\,dr$$

That means $\delta_l > 0$ for attraction, $\delta_l < 0$ for repulsion. For exchange forces $V(r)$ has the characteristic factor $(-1)^l$; that means different signs of the interaction energy for P- than for S-states. The phase δ_l will decrease with increasing l, corresponding to the decreased scattering into states of higher angular momentum. The only quantity which has been measured is the quantity

$$R = \frac{|f(\pi)|^2}{|f(\pi/2)|^2}$$

which is the ratio of the differential cross sections for scattering in the backward and the perpendicular directions, respectively, in the center of gravity system. It corresponds to the ratio of the scattering at 90 degrees

[26] N. F. Mott and H. S. W. Massey, *Theory of Atomic Collisions.* Oxford Univ. Press, London, 1933, p. 24.

[27] N. F. Mott and H. S. W. Massey, *loc. cit.*, p. 28.

to that at 45 degrees in the laboratory system of reference.

If we assume that only δ_0 and δ_1 are appreciably different from zero in this energy range, using $P_0(\cos\theta) = 1$, and $P_1(\cos\theta) = \cos\theta$, we find that

$$f(\pi/2) = (1/2ik)[e^{2i\delta_0} - 1] = (1/2ik) \times [-(1 - \cos 2\delta_0) + i \sin 2\delta_0]$$

since

$$P_1(\pi/2) = 0$$

$$f(\pi) = (1/2ik)[(e^{2i\delta_0} - 1) - 3(e^{2i\delta_1} - 1)]$$

Let us define a new quantity $f_1(\theta) = 2ikf(\theta)$. We then find

$$f_1(\pi) = f_1(\pi/2) - 3(e^{2i\delta_1} - 1)$$

$$|f_1(\pi)|^2 = |f_1(\pi/2)|^2 - 6(1 - \cos 2\delta_0) \times (1 - \cos 2\delta_1) + 9(1 - \cos 2\delta_1)^2 - 6 \sin 2\delta_0 \sin 2\delta_1 + 9 \sin^2 2\delta_1$$

If $\sin 2\delta_0 > 0$, and if $-\pi/2 < \delta_1 < 0$, then $R > 1$, while if $\sin 2\delta_0 > 0$ and $0 < \delta_1 < \pi/2$, then $R < 1$. The condition $\sin 2\delta_0 > 0$ is empirically correct. Moreover, δ_0 decreases with energy while δ_1 increases to a maximum.

With the use of the Born approximation it has been shown that if $\sin 2\delta_0 > 0$ and if δ_1 is small, then $\delta_1 > 0$ if the forces are attractive and $\delta_1 < 0$ if the forces are repulsive in the P-states. Hence it can be inferred that for the repulsive forces $R > 1$, and for attractive forces $R < 1$.

CALCULATIONS OF FERRETTI, HULTHÉN, AND JAUCH FOR THE QUANTITY R

Theory	Meson Mass (units of electron mass)	Coupling Constant	R	
			Born approximation	Exact
M–R	200	$(g_1\mu)^2 = 0.226 \quad (f\mu)^2 = 0.298$	4.21	2.21
M–R	400	$(g_1\mu)^2 = 0.226 \quad (f\mu)^2 = 0.298$	1.64	
M–R–S	$\mu_0 = 200$ $\mu_1 = 400$	$g_1 = 0 \quad (f\mu_0)^2 = 0.298$	2.44	
M–R–S	$\mu_0 = 177$ $\mu_1 = 283$	$g_1 = 0 \quad (f\mu_0)^2 = 0.298$		1.1
M–R–S	$\mu_0 = 200$ $\mu_1 = 283$	$g_1 = 0 \quad (f\mu_0)^2 = 0.298$	3.60	
Pseudoscalar	$\mu = 200$		1.84	
Neutral (Rarita–Schwinger) ($E = 15.3$ Mev)			0.525	
Neutral (cut-off radius) Bethe				0.5 to 0.8

From the experiments of Amaldi[28] and co-workers the following results were obtained:

E (in Mev)	R
12.5	0.71 ± 0.04
13.3	0.53 ± 0.03
14	0.52 ± 0.03

R is found to be less than unity in these experiments, hence they predict that the forces are attractive and not of an exchange type. Using a photographic method, Champion and Powell[29] find for a group of 13 Mev neutrons for this ratio R the value 0.67 ± 0.20. As these experiments are of so decisive a character for the theory, it would be desirable that they should be repeated with an increased accuracy.

The theoretical considerations above are based on a "weak coupling" theory. The results obtained from a "strong coupling" theory will be discussed in the next lecture.

Ferretti, Hulthén, and Jauch have carried out calculations to determine the quantity R which are given in the table on page 55. Unless otherwise stated the energy was 14.5 Mev.

Hulthén has proposed a theory using a mixture of neutral scalar and charged pseudoscalar mesons, with a larger coupling constant for the neutral scalar interaction. This will give tensor neutron–proton forces. This proposal is, however, not satisfactory because the ordinary forces are in contradiction with the saturation properties of nuclei.

[28] M. Ageno, E. Amaldi, D. Bocciarelli, and G. C. Trabacchi, *Naturwissenschaften*, **30,** 582 (1942).

[29] F. C. Champion and C. F. Powell, *Proc. Roy. Soc. London*, **A183,** 64 (1944).

CHAPTER VI

Strong Coupling Theory of the Two-Nucleon System

To obtain the interaction between nucleons in the case of strong coupling, the kinetic energy of the meson field is neglected in the zeroth approximation so that diagonalizing the energy means diagonalizing the potential energy. It was further noted in Chapter III (page 35) that the state of lowest potential energy of two nucleons in the symmetrical pseudoscalar theory is a singlet state, and that the properties of this singlet state can be expressed in the simple rule that $\tau_\alpha\sigma_k$, when operating on a singlet state, can be replaced, apart from a conventionally chosen minus sign, by the component $e_{\alpha k}$ of the vector $\mathbf{e}_\alpha$, where the three vectors $\mathbf{e}_\alpha$ are orthogonal and normalized, so that

$$(\mathbf{e}_\alpha \cdot \mathbf{e}_\beta) = \delta_{\alpha\beta}$$

and

$$\sum_\alpha e_{\alpha k} e_{\alpha l} = \delta_{kl}$$

In the pseudoscalar theory the potential energy is

$$E_{\text{pot}} = \sum_\alpha \tfrac{1}{2} \int \varphi_\alpha(\mathbf{x})(-\Delta + \mu^2)\, \varphi_\alpha(\mathbf{x}) d^3x + \sum_{A\alpha} \sqrt{4\pi} f_0 \int \varphi_\alpha(\mathbf{x})(\mathbf{e}_\alpha^A \cdot \nabla) U(\mathbf{x} - \mathbf{z}_A) d^3x$$

Comparing this with the Hamiltonian $H_0 + H_{\text{int}}$ of Chapter I, we see that the kinetic energy of the meson field

$$\tfrac{1}{2} \sum_{\alpha} \int d^3x \, \Pi_\alpha{}^2$$

has been omitted here in accordance with the approximation program, and that the second term of E_{pot} becomes H_{int} if the source function $U(\mathbf{x} - \mathbf{z}_A)$ is equal to $\delta(\mathbf{x} - \mathbf{z}_A)$(point nucleon). The equations of motion, derived from the Hamiltonian

$$\tfrac{1}{2} \int \Pi_\alpha{}^2 \, d^3x + E_{\text{pot}}$$

combine to the equation

$$\left(-\nabla^2 + \mu^2 + \frac{\partial^2}{\partial t^2} \right) \varphi_\alpha = - f_0 \sqrt{4\pi} \sum_A (\mathbf{e}_\alpha^A \cdot \boldsymbol{\nabla}) U(\mathbf{x} - \mathbf{z}_A)$$

where $\boldsymbol{\nabla}$ operates on $\mathbf{x}$. The static solution φ_α of this equation, defined by $\partial \varphi_\alpha^{\text{stat}} / \partial t = 0$, is

$$\varphi_\alpha^{\text{stat}} = - (f_0/\sqrt{4\pi}) \sum_A (\mathbf{e}_\alpha^A \cdot \boldsymbol{\nabla}) \, \chi \, (\mathbf{x} - \mathbf{z}_A)$$

where

$$\chi(\mathbf{x}) = \int U(\mathbf{x}')(e^{-\mu r}/r) d^3x'$$

with $r = |\mathbf{x} - \mathbf{x}'|$. Inserting this solution in the potential energy we have

$$\begin{aligned} E_{\text{pot}} = \sum_\alpha \tfrac{1}{2} \int & \Big[(f_0/\sqrt{4\pi}) \sum_B (\mathbf{e}_\alpha^B \cdot \boldsymbol{\nabla}) \, \chi \, (\mathbf{x} - \mathbf{z}_B) \Big] \times \\ & \Big[f_0 \sqrt{4\pi} \sum_A (\mathbf{e}_\alpha^A \cdot \boldsymbol{\nabla}) \, U \, (\mathbf{x} - \mathbf{z}_A) \Big] \, d^3x \\ - \sum_{A\alpha} \sqrt{4\pi} \, f_0 \int & \Big[(f_0/\sqrt{4\pi}) \sum_B (\mathbf{e}_\alpha^B \cdot \boldsymbol{\nabla}) \, \chi \, (\mathbf{x} - \mathbf{z}_B) \Big] \times \\ & (\mathbf{e}_\alpha^A \cdot \boldsymbol{\nabla}) \, U \, (\mathbf{x} - \mathbf{z}_A) \, d^3x \\ = (f_0{}^2/2) \sum_{\alpha AB} \int & [(\mathbf{e}_\alpha^B \cdot \boldsymbol{\nabla}) \, \chi \, (\mathbf{x} - \mathbf{z}_B)] \times \\ & [(\mathbf{e}_\alpha^A \cdot \boldsymbol{\nabla}) \, U \, (\mathbf{x} - \mathbf{z}_A)] \, d^3x \\ - f_0{}^2 \sum_{\alpha AB} \int & [(\mathbf{e}_\alpha^B \cdot \boldsymbol{\nabla}) \, \chi \, (\mathbf{x} - \mathbf{z}_B)][(\mathbf{e}_\alpha^A \cdot \boldsymbol{\nabla}) \, U \, (\mathbf{x} - \mathbf{z}_A)] \, d^3x \end{aligned}$$

Considering first the self-energy E we have, summing over α

$$E = -\tfrac{1}{2} f_0^2 \sum_A \int (\nabla\chi^A)\cdot(\nabla U^A)\, d^3x$$

where

$$\chi^A = \chi(\mathbf{x} - \mathbf{z}_A), \quad U^A = U(\mathbf{x} - \mathbf{z}_A)$$

Using the Fourier integral for $U(\mathbf{x})$ and for $e^{-\mu r}/r$ we obtain

$$E = -\frac{f_0^2}{(2\pi)^2} \sum_A \int d^3k \frac{k^2}{k^2 + \mu^2} G(\mathbf{k})$$

according to the definition of $G(\mathbf{k})$ in Chapter II, page 13 (see also Chapter III, page 36). This can be written as

$$E = -\frac{f_0^2}{(2\pi)^2} \sum_A \left\{ \int d^3k\, G(\mathbf{k}) - \mu^2 \int d^3k \frac{1}{k^2 + \mu^2} G(\mathbf{k}) \right\}$$

Assuming spherical symmetry for U and G, we obtain

$$E = -\frac{f_0^2}{(2\pi)^2} \sum_A \left\{ 4\pi \int_0^\infty k^2 dk\, G(k) - 4\pi\mu^2 \int_0^\infty \frac{k^2 dk}{k^2 + \mu^2} G(k) \right\}$$

$$= -f_0^2 \sum_A \left\{ \frac{N}{2} - \frac{\mu^2}{2a} + \frac{\mu^4}{\pi} \int_0^\infty \frac{dk}{k^2 + \mu^2} G(k) \right\}.$$

using the quantities N and a defined in Chapter II, page 17. Since the last integral is convergent we may replace $G(k)$ by unity and thus obtain for the *self-energy per heavy particle*

$$E = -f_0^2 C/2$$

with

$$C = N - (\mu^2/a) + \mu^3$$

The *interaction energy* $\sum_{AB}' V_{AB}$, is obtained in a similar way from the above.

$$\sum_{AB}' V_{AB} = -(f_0^2/2) \sum_{\alpha AB}' \int [(\mathbf{e}_\alpha^A \cdot \nabla)\chi^B][(\mathbf{e}_\alpha^B \cdot \nabla) U^A]\, d^3x$$

$$= +\frac{f_0^2}{(2\pi)^5} \sum_{\alpha AB}' \int d^3x \int (\mathbf{e}_\alpha^A \cdot \mathbf{k}) \frac{v(\mathbf{k})}{k^2 + \mu^2} e^{i\mathbf{k}\cdot(\mathbf{x}-\mathbf{z}_A)}\, d^3k \times$$
$$\int (\mathbf{e}_\alpha^B \cdot \mathbf{k}')\, v(\mathbf{k}')\, e^{i\mathbf{k}'\cdot(\mathbf{x}-\mathbf{z}_B)}\, d^3k'$$

$$= -\frac{f_0^2}{(2\pi)^2} \sum_{\alpha AB}' \int d^3k (\mathbf{e}_\alpha^A \cdot \mathbf{k}) \frac{v(\mathbf{k})}{k^2 + \mu^2} e^{-i(\mathbf{k}\cdot\mathbf{z}_A)} \times$$
$$(\mathbf{e}_\alpha^B \cdot \mathbf{k})\, v(-\mathbf{k})\, e^{i(\mathbf{k}\mathbf{z}_B)}$$

$$= -\frac{f_0^2}{(2\pi)^2} \sum_{\alpha AB}' (\mathbf{e}_\alpha^A \cdot \nabla_A)(\mathbf{e}_\alpha^B \cdot \nabla_B) \int d^3k \frac{G(\mathbf{k})}{k^2 + \mu^2} e^{i\mathbf{k}(\mathbf{z}_B - \mathbf{z}_A)}$$

where the prime indicates $A \neq B$. As long as the distance $|\mathbf{z}_B - \mathbf{z}_A|$ is not too small we can replace $v(\mathbf{k})v(-\mathbf{k}) = G(\mathbf{k})$ by unity and obtain

$$\sum_{AB}' V_{AB} = -\frac{f_0^2}{2} \sum_{\alpha AB}' (\mathbf{e}_\alpha^A \cdot \nabla_A)(\mathbf{e}_\alpha^B \cdot \nabla_B) \frac{e^{-\mu|\mathbf{z}_B - \mathbf{z}_A|}}{|\mathbf{z}_B - \mathbf{z}_A|}$$

so that the *interaction energy between two nucleons*, A and B, becomes

$$V_{AB} = -f_0^2 \sum_\alpha (\mathbf{e}_\alpha^A \cdot \nabla_A)(\mathbf{e}_\alpha^B \cdot \nabla_B) \frac{e^{-\mu|\mathbf{z}_B - \mathbf{z}_A|}}{|\mathbf{z}_B - \mathbf{z}_A|}$$

The lowest eigenvalue which we have considered here splits up into isobar states in the next approximation. These isobar states have been described classically in Chapter II (pages 23 *et seq.*) for the neutral pseudoscalar field. In the symmetrical pseudoscalar case treated here the three vectors $\mathbf{e}_\alpha$ play the role of the vector $\boldsymbol{\sigma}$ of the above calculation. The quantum-mechanical treatment[30] results in an isobar energy term in the Hamiltonian given by[31]

$$(\epsilon/2) \sum_A (\mathbf{S}_A{}^2 - \tfrac{3}{4})$$

where

$$\epsilon = 3a/2f_0{}^2$$

S is defined in terms of the Euler angles defining $e_{\alpha k}$ such that if, $e_{\alpha k}$ is given by the values in the table on page 62,

S is given by

$$S_1 = -\sin\varphi p_\theta + \frac{\cos\varphi}{\sin\theta}(p_\psi - \cos\theta \cdot p_\varphi)$$

$$S_2 = \cos\varphi\, p_\theta + \frac{\sin\varphi}{\sin\theta}(p_\psi - \cos\theta \cdot p_\varphi)$$

$$S_3 = p_\varphi$$

$$\mathbf{S}^2 = \frac{1}{\sin\theta} p_\theta \sin\theta\, p_\theta + \frac{(p_\psi - \cos\theta\, p_\varphi)^2}{\sin^2\theta} + p_\varphi{}^2$$

with

$$p_\theta = -i\frac{\partial}{\partial\theta},\ p_\varphi = -i\frac{\partial}{\partial\varphi},\ p_\psi = -i\frac{\partial}{\partial\psi}$$

From these equations follow the commutation rules:

[30] W. Pauli and S. M. Dancoff, *Phys. Rev.*, **62,** 85 (1942).

[31] This term is mathematically identical to the kinetic energy of a spherical top.

$$[e_{\alpha 1}, S_2] = [S_1, e_{\alpha 2}] = ie_{\alpha 3}$$
$$[e_{\alpha 1}, S_1] = 0$$
$$[S_1, S_2] = i\, S_3$$

and their cyclic analogues.

$\alpha \backslash k$	1	2	3
1	$\cos\theta\cos\varphi\cos\psi - \sin\varphi\sin\psi$	$\cos\theta\sin\varphi\cos\psi + \cos\varphi\sin\psi$	$-\sin\theta\cos\psi$
2	$-\cos\theta\cos\varphi\sin\psi - \sin\varphi\cos\psi$	$-\cos\theta\sin\varphi\sin\psi + \cos\varphi\cos\psi$	$\sin\theta\sin\psi$
3	$\sin\theta\cos\varphi$	$\sin\theta\sin\varphi$	$\cos\theta$

In the case of the Møller–Rosenfeld–Schwinger mixture the interaction energy becomes instead

$$V_{AB} = \sum_{\alpha} (\mathbf{e}_{\alpha A}\cdot\nabla)(\mathbf{e}_{\alpha B}\cdot\nabla)\,[f_0^2\,(e^{-\mu_0 r}/r) - f_1^2\,(e^{-\mu_1 r}/r)] + (\mathbf{e}_{\alpha A}\cdot\mathbf{e}_{\alpha B})\,f_1^2\,\mu_1^2\,(e^{-\mu_1 r}/r)$$

and the value of ϵ is then

$$\epsilon = \frac{3a}{2(f_0^2 + 2f_1^2)}$$

The subscript "zero," as before, denotes terms arising from the pseudoscalar field, and the subscript "one," terms due to the vector field. The latter is characterized by two coupling constants, g_1 for the longitudinal component, and f_1 for the transverse components of the vector field. The longitudinal part does not contribute.

The total Hamiltonian for the heavy particles is in this approximation

$$H = (\epsilon/2) \sum_A (\mathbf{S}_A{}^2 - \tfrac{3}{4}) + \sum_{AB} V_{AB} + (1/2M) \sum_A p_A{}^2$$

V_{AB} has transition elements to isobaric states. If the distance between two nucleons and their isobaric separation is sufficiently small, the state of the system can be described as an oscillation of the **e**-vectors about their stable equilibrium, which is given by the minimum of V_{AB}.[32]

Fierz and Wentzel[33] have investigated the simpler case

$$V_{AB} = \sum_\alpha (\mathbf{e}_{\alpha A} \cdot \mathbf{e}_{\alpha B}) \; V\,(r_{AB})$$

omitting the tensor forces. In this case the stable equilibrium is achieved for

$$\mathbf{e}_{\alpha B} = -\,\mathbf{e}_{\alpha A}$$

if $V(r_{AB})$ is positive and $\mathbf{e}_{\alpha B} = \mathbf{e}_{\alpha A}$ if V is negative. For an interaction of this type $V(r_{AB})$ must, therefore, be positive, because otherwise there would be no saturation for higher nuclei.

The neutral theory leads to attraction when the **e**-vectors are parallel to each other and perpendicular to the line connecting the nucleons. A stable equilibrium would therefore exist when all nucleons are arranged in a plane with the **e**-vectors parallel, which is, of course, to be excluded because of the known spins of heavy nuclei. A problem still to be investigated is whether

[32] See R. Serber and S. M. Dancoff, *Phys. Rev.*, **63,** 143 (1943).

[33] M. Fierz and G. Wentzel, *Helv. Phys. Acta*, **17,** 215 (1944). M. Fierz, *ibid.*, **17,** 181 (1944). G. Wentzel, *ibid.*, **17,** 252 (1944). Compare also *ibid.*, **16,** 222, 551 (1943). The most general states of the deuteron are investigated by K. Bleuler, *ibid.*, **17,** 405 (1944); **18,** 317 (1945).

one would gain too much energy by replacing protons or neutrons with negative nucleons, so that the theoretical nuclear charge of a nucleus of a given mass would become too small. In the Fermi–Thomas model this question can be answered in the negative,[34] but this statistical method is not quite justifiable.

In the case of the Schwinger "mixture" (Chapter I, page 9), the following constants are used:

$$\mu_0 = 177\, m, \quad \mu_1 = 2\mu_0$$

$$f_0 = f_1 = f$$

$$(f\mu_0)^2 = 0.375, \quad a\mu_0 = 0.1$$

In this case the separation of the two lowest isobar states is $3\epsilon/2$, which is about ten times the binding energy of the deuteron (2.17 Mev). The excitation energy of the isobars is then a small perturbation compared to V_{AB} at nuclear ranges.

Apart from the vanishing of the magnetic moment of the deuteron, the strong coupling theory does not introduce difficulties. For weak coupling the magnetic moment is not given correctly either, and to remove this difficulty an intermediate coupling would have to be introduced.

It was shown in Chapter V (pages 56 *et seq.*) that, in order to explain the scattering experiments of Amaldi *et al.*, an attractive nonexchange force has to be assumed, on the basis of a weak coupling theory. This, of course, would be in contradiction with the stability of heavy nuclei. In the strong coupling theory without tensor forces (Wentzel), one has for P-scattering large

[34] F. Coester, *Helv. Phys. Acta*, **17**, 35 (1944).

distance repulsion and small distance attraction. Taking the tensor forces into account,[35] Wentzel[36] has investigated the problem of the anisotropy of the neutron–proton scattering in more detail from the standpoint of the strong coupling theory, in which the idea of the charge independence of the nucleon interactions is rigorously maintained. He finds $R = 0.6$ for a value $\epsilon = 30$ Mev. It has still to be tested, however, whether the assumptions of this theory are in agreement with other observed properties of the deuteron, as, for instance, with the fact that the ^1S-state is virtual.

Concluding Remarks

There are, at present, essentially two ways of approaching the problem of nuclear forces: (*1*) the nonrelativistic theory with finite size nucleons; (*2*) the relativistic theory.[37] Meson-pair theories have not been considered here.

The relativistic theory without "cutting off" failed. With the use of the λ-limiting process it also failed, because the magnetic moment of the proton becomes less than unity and the neutron moment becomes positive. In order to explain the quadrupole moment of the deuteron relativistic terms were required, which even in the mixed theory become infinite, of order r^{-3}.[38]

[35] Compare the evaluation of the corresponding matrix elements of the interaction energy by M. Fierz, *Helv. Phys. Acta*, **18,** 158 (1945).

[36] G. Wentzel, *ibid.*, **18,** 430 (1945).

[37] "Relativistic" and "nonrelativistic" refer to the treatment of the nucleons, since the meson must always be described relativistically.

[38] N. Hu, *Phys. Rev.*, **67,** 339 (1945).

It appears that, at the present time, the more restricted first approach—i.e., disregarding the demand of relativistic invariance—is more hopeful. In this theory, neither the weak nor the strong coupling approximation yields correct values for the magnetic moments of the nucleons, but intermediate coupling might give the correct results.

The most urgently needed experimental data are, at present, data on neutron–proton scattering, particularly its angular distribution, and the decision of the question whether stable isobars exist, the answer to the second question being a clue to the magnitude of the quantity a.

APPENDIX

We have yet to show how a given spin motion radiates mesons. This process is described by the Kirchhoff equation (page 14, equation 1) for the meson field written in momentum space as

$$\frac{\partial^2 \tilde{q}(\mathbf{k})}{\partial t^2} + (k^2 + \mu^2)\, \tilde{q}(\mathbf{k}) = \frac{if}{\pi\sqrt{2}} G(\mathbf{k})(\boldsymbol{\sigma}\cdot\mathbf{k})$$

The general solution of this equation is

$$\tilde{q}(\mathbf{k}) = \tilde{q}_i\,(\mathbf{k}) + \sum_{\nu} \tilde{q}_\nu\, e^{-i\nu}$$

where $\nu = +\omega, -\omega$, $\tilde{q}_i(\mathbf{k})$ is the solution of the homogeneous equation representing the incident plane wave (page 26) and

$$\tilde{q}_\nu = \frac{if}{\pi\sqrt{2}} \frac{G(\mathbf{k})}{k^2 + \mu^2 - \nu^2} (\boldsymbol{\sigma}_\nu \cdot \mathbf{k})$$

To obtain the wave function $\varphi_\nu^s(\mathbf{x})$ of the scattered mesons due to $\boldsymbol{\sigma}_\nu$, in coordinate space, we have to evaluate

$$\varphi_\nu^s\,(\mathbf{x}) = \frac{1}{(2\pi)^{3/2}} \int q_\nu\, e^{i\mathbf{k}\cdot\mathbf{x}}\, d^3k$$

where

$$q_\nu = \tilde{q}_\nu / v\,(-\mathbf{k})$$

or

$$\varphi_\nu^s(\mathbf{x}) = \frac{1}{(2\pi)^{3/2}} \int_0^\infty k^2\, dk \int_0^\pi \sin\theta\, d\theta \int_0^{2\pi} d\varphi\, q_\nu\, e^{ikr\cos\theta}$$

where θ, φ are the polar angles of $\mathbf{k}$ with respect to $\mathbf{x}$ and $\mathbf{x} = r\mathbf{n}_s$. Integrating first over the angles we have

$$J = \int_0^\pi \sin\theta\, d\theta \int_0^{2\pi} d\varphi\, q_\nu\, e^{ikr\cos\theta} =$$

$$\int_{-1}^{1} d\xi\, e^{ikr\xi} \int_0^{2\pi} d\varphi \frac{if}{\pi\sqrt{2}} v(\mathbf{k}) \frac{(\boldsymbol{\sigma}_\nu \cdot \mathbf{k})}{k^2 + \mu^2 - \nu^2}$$

We have previously assumed that $U(\mathbf{x})$ depends only on r, so that $v(\mathbf{k})$ depends only on k and not on the direction of $\mathbf{k}$. We write $(\boldsymbol{\sigma}_\nu \cdot \mathbf{k})$ as

$$(\boldsymbol{\sigma}_\nu \cdot \mathbf{k}) = \sigma_\nu k\, [\sin\theta \sin\theta' \cos(\varphi - \varphi') + \cos\theta \cos\theta']$$

where θ', φ' are the polar angles of $\boldsymbol{\sigma}_\nu$ with respect to $\mathbf{x}$. The first term vanishes, when integrated over φ, and we obtain

$$J = 2\pi \frac{if}{\pi\sqrt{2}} v(k) \frac{\sigma_\nu k \cos\theta'}{k^2 + \mu^2 - \nu^2} \int_{-1}^{1} d\xi\, \xi e^{ikr\xi}$$

$$= 2\pi \frac{if}{\pi\sqrt{2}} v(k) \frac{\sigma_\nu \cos\theta'}{k^2 + \mu^2 - \nu^2} \frac{1}{i} \frac{\partial}{\partial r} \int_{-1}^{1} d\xi\, e^{ikr\xi}$$

$$= f\sqrt{2} \cdot v(k) \frac{\sigma_\nu \cos \cdot \theta'}{k^2 + \mu^2 - \nu^2} \cdot \left\{ \frac{e^{ikr} + e^{-ikr}}{r} + \text{(higher powers of } r^{-1}) \right\}$$

and therefore

$$\varphi_\nu^s(\mathbf{x}) \sim \frac{1}{(2\pi)^{3/2}} \cdot f\sqrt{2}\sigma_\nu \cos\theta' \int_0^\infty \frac{v(k)\, k^2}{k^2 - K^2} \frac{e^{ikr} + e^{-ikr}}{r} dk$$

$$\sim \frac{1}{(2\pi)^{3/2}} \cdot f\sqrt{2}\, \sigma_\nu \cos\theta' \int_{-\infty}^{\infty} \frac{v(k)\, k^2}{k^2 - K^2} \frac{e^{ikr}}{r} dk$$

In order to obtain outgoing waves only in coordinate space the path of integration has to be taken in the k-plane as shown in Chapter II, on page 18. Assuming $v(k)$ to be regular in a finite strip above the real axis, we close the path of integration around $k = K$, and obtain

$$\varphi_\nu^s(x) \sim \frac{1}{(2\pi)^{3/2}} f \sqrt{2}\, \sigma_\nu \cos\theta' \, 2\pi i \, \frac{v(K)K}{2} \frac{e^{iKr}}{r}$$

The amplitude for scattering in the direction $\mathbf{n}_s$ is, therefore,

$$A_s^{(\nu)} = (2\pi)^{-3/2} i f \pi \sqrt{2}\, K\, v(K)(\boldsymbol{\sigma}_\nu \cdot \mathbf{n}_s)$$

or

$$A_s^{(\nu)} = (\mathbf{B}_\nu \cdot \mathbf{n}_s)$$

where

$$\mathbf{B}_\nu = (2\pi)^{-3/2} i f \pi \sqrt{2}\, K\, v(K) \boldsymbol{\sigma}_\nu$$